P9-ECT-127

Date Due

MAR 26 1974		
MAY 1 3 '66		AR 2 2 10
FEB 3 '6	MAY 2 0 1970	
APR 21 '67	NO 3 '7 JE 5'9	MY 1 3 '10
MAY 2 8 '67	NO 19 '0	
JUN 2 '67 JY 20		
MR 15 '68	DEC 15 '6	AP 2 2 '94
MAR 2 2 '6		
AP 19 '88	P 28 OC 12 '9	
MY 17 '68	JE 2 '7 NO 20	
JE 13 '69	UE 8	
JE 19 '70		

N
6410
H34

RIVERSIDE CITY COLLEGE
LIBRARY
Riverside, California

bd PRINTED IN U.S.A.

NEO-CLASSICISM
Style and Motif

NEO-CLASSICISM
Style and Motif

BY

Henry Hawley

WITH AN ESSAY BY

Rémy G. Saisselin

The Cleveland Museum of Art

DISTRIBUTED BY HARRY N. ABRAMS, INC., NEW YORK CITY

Riverside City College Library
Riverside, California

N6410 .H34 1964
Hawley, Henry.
Neo-classicism : style and
motif

BOARD OF TRUSTEES

George P. Bickford   Severance A. Millikin
Harold T. Clark   Mrs. R. Henry Norweb
James H. Dempsey, Jr.   A. Dean Perry
Robert I. Gale, Jr.   Ralph S. Schmitt
Edgar A. Hahn   James N. Sherwin
Mrs. David S. Ingalls   John S. Wilbur
James D. Ireland   Lewis B. Williams
Charles B. Bolton, *Emeritus*

Copyright 1964 by The Cleveland Museum of Art
University Circle, Cleveland, Ohio 44106
Library of Congress Catalogue Card Number 64-24988
Printed in the United States of America

Distributed by Harry N. Abrams, Inc., New York

Acknowledgments

PERHAPS no Western art style is so little known and understood in its entirety as Neo-classicism. The work of a few artists—David, Ingres, Soane—and some varieties of the products made in the style—Wedgwood ceramics, Louis XVI furniture—have recently been highly valued, but in comparison to what contemporaries felt to be the significant contributions made in their time, our present interests appear extremely limited. Is our view the result of a justifiable pruning away of artistic deadwood following the dictates of the legitimate application of historical perspective in determining the importance of works of art made in the past, or might our neglect of Neo-classicism have been caused by our misunderstanding of its objectives and our ignorance, at first hand, of many of its efforts? In order to answer questions such as this, a re-examination of the evidence is necessary. An opportunity for at least a partial re-examination is offered here.

It has for some time been accepted that the styles in the visual arts which are called Neo-classicism and Romanticism are probably very closely related in terms of the attitudes and conditions of society which produced them and which they reflect. However, to facilitate an examination of the earlier of these two tendencies, the group of objects assembled here has been rather arbitrarily limited to works which are both Neo-classic in style and are based in subject upon classical sources or incorporate into their designs Graeco-Roman decorative motifs. Only a few exceptions to this rule have been allowed in cases where no other works were available by artists who needed to be included. It is hoped that by so limiting the selection, stylistic development and the interrelation of national schools—subjects which are amplified upon in the accompanying introductory essays—will be made clearer.

The labor and cooperation of many persons was necessary in order to transform this exhibition from an idea to a reality. I should like to thank, first of all, the lenders, both private and institutional, without whose generosity it would have been impossible to assemble this exhibition. They have not only entrusted to us for a time the works of art which are their responsibility, but have supplied much of the data used in writing this catalogue. My special thanks go to Anthony M. Clark, Thomas J. McCormick, and John Maxon, who have been most generous in lending from their private collections and the public collections which are in their charge, and, in addition, have been extremely kind in sharing with me their knowledge of Neo-classicism. Among the members of the staff of the Cleveland Museum, I wish to thank, first, Rémy Saisselin, who supplied one of the essays contained herein and notes for many of the biographical sketches of artists. Mrs. Frances Saha, my secretary, has not only typed the manuscript of this catalogue, but assumed much responsibility for the correspondence attendant to this exhibition. Mrs. Margaret Marcus helped with the preparation of the catalogue entries. Richard Godfrey and his staff in the Photography Studio have worked very hard to make the necessary special photographs. The Registrar, Lillian Kern, and her staff have taken charge of details of shipping and insurance for objects included in the exhibition. Merald Wrolstad, with his accustomed skill, has acted as editor and designer of this catalogue. The installation of the works of art has been in the capable hands of the Museum's designer, William E. Ward. The above named are only a few of the staff members who have aided in this effort. To all of them, my gratitude.

HENRY HAWLEY

June 12, 1964

Contents

Neo-classicism: Virtue, Reason and Nature

Rémy G. Saisselin

I ADMIT MY TASTE for the Ancients. Antiquity enchants me, and I am always moved to say with Pliny: 'You are going to Athens. Respect their Gods.' " Thus wrote the President de Montesquieu in one of his notebooks. When he looked about him and considered his contemporaries, he thought the world had lost the smiling air it possessed in the times of Greece and Rome. Such sentiments, expressed by a distinguished man of letters in a time still dominated by the Rococo taste, are as good as any to begin a consideration of the Neo-classic style. For a style, as one French art historian put it, "C'est à la fois des motifs et un esprit." The spirit of the Neo-classic was rather well expressed by Montesquieu, and others, long before the motifs gave it form, and as the spirit, so the motifs were found in the past. We may say at the outset then that the Neo-classic was in part an attempt to revive the past and relive it by way of the doctrine of the imitation of the Ancients. Men had been in search of lost time before Proust, and by the end of the eighteenth century it was not only one man who was concerned with his own past which catches our attention, but an entire society.

The relation of the past to the Neo-classic has been stressed by several noted scholars.[1] It can, indeed, hardly be overstressed. It was a sense of the past which made the men of the eighteenth century more and more interested in history and archaeology; it was a wider knowledge of the past which altered their style of construction, designing, picturing, gesturing, posing, dressing, and eloquence; as it was also this increased knowledge which eventually must destroy that other craving of the times, the belief in or assumption of the existence of a universally valid taste and beauty. However, it must not be supposed that this sense of the past meant for the men of the late eighteenth century what later came to be known as historical relativism. On the contrary, it was accompanied by a sense of the eternal. The sense of the dying away of all civilizations was countered by the belief, voiced for example in Volney's *Ruins*, that history was governed by eternal rules: the providence of the Christian world was replaced by the notion of history, which was construed as a compound of natural and moral law. Voltaire and Gibbon both wrote that history was a record of the crimes, follies, and misfortunes of mankind, but this did not preclude a sense of law. *L'Esprit des lois* and the *Scienza Nuova* are studies of the past, demonstrating that it is not governed by caprice. In the realm of the fine arts, the Neo-classic style represents the same sense of law and reason.

1

In the realm of morality, this sense of law and reason turned into a purist's vision of nature. Indeed, the sense of the past was curiously ambiguous. The past supplied models for the arts and for moral duty, but history also demonstrated that a pure nature had been lost. Rousseau, for example, considered history as a falling away from a state of nature in which men had been innocent and free. The arts and sciences had become necessary in order to hide the vices created by civilization, which had been established with the accidental foundation of private property. For Winckelmann, who is to the fine arts what Rousseau is to nature and morality, a good deal of the art which came into existence since the Greeks could only be construed as a degenerate form of the pure models established by the Ancients. To be sure, Winckelmann was enamored of Athens and Rousseau of Sparta, but they were both united in a desire they held in common with their contemporaries, that of purity, one of style for Winckelmann, one of morality for Rousseau. One thus comes to readily understand why the French Revolution was thought of in terms of a rebirth; for this desire for purity can be construed as a nostalgia for and a desire to regain a lost non-Christian paradise.

Consequently this style can also be considered as an emanation of the Enlightenment. The style was justified not only in terms of past examples, but also by Reason and Nature: Greece, Rome, Reason, Nature, and the virtue of the Roman citizen were confused in the minds of the men of the later eighteenth century. Thus, though the motifs were drawn from the classical past, the *esprit* of the Neo-classic style was essentially eighteenth century. One might even joke and say it was essentialist, which would be one way of answering the question which immediately comes to mind when we say it was essentially eighteenth century: which one?

For there was, as well we know, more than one eighteenth century. There were, to begin with, at least two. If you are an art historian there was that of the Rococo and that of the Neo-classic, separate, mixed and co-existing. If you are a literary historian of the old school, there was that of Reason and Sentiment, of Voltaire and Rousseau, Montesquieu and Diderot. If you are a literary historian and critic of the newer school, you are much less sure that there were only two, and if you are a *comparatiste* you know very well there were more than two.[2] If you are an historian *tout court* you know very well there may have been more than three. Modes of thinking survived which were more medieval in nature than modern; a modern state machinery functioned along with institutions which had survived for long centuries; men are governed by habits, vanity, pride, and passion rather than by reason, so that when it comes to assessing the luminosity of the Enlightenment it is necessary to be very careful. The *Spirit of the age*, that neat Hegelian abstraction—invented, it is true, by the eighteenth century—varied geographically: *les Lumières* meant one thing in France; *Aufklärung*, something else in Germany, where it was one thing in Prussia and another in Frankfort-am-Main and again something else in Dresden and Leipzig. The Enlightenment in Britain was different from the above, and again quite different in Italy, where it never reached the Venetian Republic and shone with but diminished and reflected force in Tuscany. In Russia it was merely the personal publicity of Catherine the Great. If you are a Marxist the temptation is to distinguish between the style of the aristocracy—decaying, frivolous, corrupt, and ruined—and the style of the rising bourgeoi-

2

sie—hard-working, conquering. The former style is the Rococo, the latter the Neo-classic. The thesis can be amply supported by reading history backwards: the Neo-classic was, par excellence, the style of the Revolution and the Empire, which were bourgeois manifestations of history.

Styles, however, have a certain disconcerting independence from rational considerations or views of the past. When Montesquieu expressed his intimate sentiments on Antiquity he was not writing or thinking as the man who wrote the *Esprit des lois*. The Neo-classic style was born of a sentiment for Antiquity (which had existed long before certain men thought they had at last found the proper and true motifs to give it form). This sentiment gradually became an *esprit*, a general taste, and finally turned into a generalized style. Reason in this development served as a tool of both heart and mind, as well as an ideal, while nature, sometimes confused with reason, also served as a moral imperative or justification. Thus the rather abstract ideas associated with the Enlightenment were given form; they were fixed, and delimited the terms reason, nature, beauty, virtue: the philosophers were given an antique air. The curious and surprising result is that the idea of progress which is so often associated with the Enlightenment in this sense turns out to be progress backward to the Greeks who had lived in a world where reason and nature were splendidly united under fortunate and ever serene skies.[3] This paradox of progress in reverse can be resolved by recalling that for the men of the Enlightenment, Greek and Roman civilization represented the high points of human achievement: progress could thus be achieved by a proper imitation of the Ancients.

This construction of a happy past and its resurrection was animated by an enthusiasm akin to religious sentiment. The Enlightenment may have been anti-Christian in orientation and in much of its prose; but it was not irreligious. Voltaire was no atheist. His sarcasm, satire, and venom were directed at an institution, its abuses and absurdities. It was largely due to the historical situation of his day that he saw the *Infâme* above all in the Church. Rousseau, on the other hand, is an example of religiosity which found it could thrive outside the institution challenged by Voltaire. Thus for those who no longer found solace in the Church and the Christian life, there remained the moral world of human action which came to be summed up in the term Humanity, and for others, there was Nature. The Neo-classic revival then is inseparable from a moral revival, a curious compound of sentiment, sentimentalism, cries for virtue, tears, and a civic sense.[4] The men of the later eighteenth century, by confusing the cult of the Antique with that of Nature, attempted to eat their cake and have it too. It worked for a while, but they choked in 1793.

Before the Neo-classic could become a generalized style the dominant taste had to be discredited. The disgrace of the Rococo preceded the elaboration of the new style. The Rococo—*rocaille*, or *chicorée*, as Cochin called it—began to be satirized in the 1740's. This critique of the Rococo or *le goût du jour* is to be found in various discourses and satires. It is dismissed or ridiculed as a mere passing fashion, as unreasonable, tasteless fancy, and as imagination run wild. Cochin and Caylus were precursors in this critique; they were echoed by men of letters.[5] This critique of current fashions was paralleled insofar as painting was concerned by Caylus' campaign to reinforce academic doctrine, the foundation of the Ecole des élèves protégés, his

3

creation of a *Prix d'expression*, and his boosting of history painting. However, it was a far cry from the satire of *chicorée* and *bibelots* to the creation of a new style. Need it be said that the stylistic critique of the Rococo was paralleled by a critique of the mores and manners of the society associated with the *chicorée?* Rousseau's *First Discourse* is an indictment of the civility prevalent at the time, of *politesse mondaine*, wit, wigs, silk stockings, ribbons—all of which he considered clever artifices hiding the true man. And he called for a new man just as others called for a new style.

A counter-style was soon to be offered. The *Essai sur l'architecture* of the Abbé Laugier, published in 1753, marks an important date as does also the very important discovery of the Doric style.[6] Greek architecture was found to be simple, natural, and rational. Indeed, in the 50's and 60's a flood of books appeared which furnished architects and decorators with new models of architecture and decoration.[7] The writings of Winckelmann also were of great weight, for he supplied a renovated doctrine of art where Cochin and others had offered merely satire. Rome plays as important a role here as does the newly discovered Greek Doric, and no consideration of the Neo-classic could be complete without mention of the architectural books of Piranesi.[8] But Rome is important in another sense; it was once more a school for painters and architects and also of the new type of amateur, the antiquarian. For those interested in the Greek style, Naples and Sicily would be of greater interest, and it is noteworthy that a reform of the French Academy in Rome now made possible trips to Naples for the students of painting, architecture, and sculpture. By the 1780's *chicorée* seemed completely wilted. Boucher, Natoire, Fragonard, Van Loo, and their followers were recognized to have been painters of a corrupt and false taste.[9] Vien was lauded in France as the reformer of painting, much as Rousseau was to be recognized as one of the men embodying the new virtue. In Rome Mengs passed as an oracle. Soon David would be recognized as the perfect embodiment of the new spirit. Vien under the Empire would become a senator. Painters had a new sense of their worth and dignity; they were citizens who played a moral role in society. The painting of history—which had fallen into neglect—was resuscitated, and art was finally moral, natural, and reasonable. At the same time the Academy had once more become a force in the artistic life of the nation.

The Neo-classic was in part the creation of men of letters, of *savants* and *raisonneurs*; it was perfectly suited to Academic teaching. Vien was praised for his knowledge of costume and his understanding of history. It was a pity his laudators had to recognize that his paintings were somewhat cold. But the Neo-classic was suited to something else, also a product of the Enlightenment—the national state conceived no longer in terms of a monarchy in which the king ruled by divine right over his subjects, but in which a sovereign, either a king or representatives of a national will, ruled over citizens. Thus it might also be argued that the Neo-classic was the prototype of a new form of official art.[10]

Possessing a thoroughly rational aesthetic, the Neo-classic was an eminently teachable style. It was eloquently expressed by Winckelmann; expounded in the superb style of Reynolds' *Discourses*; consecrated in the *Dictionnaire des arts de peinture, sculpture et gravure* of Watelet, published in 1792. It can also be argued that it even found metaphysical justification in Kant's

Critique of the Aesthetic Judgement, for there are indications enough to show that the philosopher of Königsberg wrote that work as if the Neo-classic were the ultimate art, in fact, Art—inseparable from civilization. That this style should lend itself to a rational aesthetic is not surprising: Winckelmann had been a classical scholar before he went to Rome and he continually quoted Plato. The *beau idéal* of Watelet's dictionary has certain affinities with a Platonic concept of beauty, and the perfect models of the Greeks are in fact the artistic manifestation and approximation of this beauty which is after all purely mental, perfect only in the mind. The *beau idéal* is essentially the philosophers' concept of beauty; it is they who are *épris de pureté,* enamoured of rationality and universality; they, too, who ever put mind over the grosser sense perceptions. Winckelmann's *tour de force* consisted in fixing this abstract beauty of the philosophers unto certain Greek models which thereby acquired the authority of universally valid canons, and the variations of taste and the relativity of beauty were thereby surmounted and, paradoxically, history denied.[11] But history could be denied only by a self-delusion created by language. The Neo-classic style, its aesthetic, and its artistic doctrine were discussed in an abstract language borrowed from philosophy and whose vocabulary had hardly changed since Plato and Aristotle. The words beauty, taste, sublime were used as they had been for a long time, but they never meant quite the same thing: beauty meant one thing in 1650, something else in 1700, and something else again in 1780. The word remained the same, but the forms associated with it differed. A rational aesthetic doctrine built on words tied to specific artistic canons and universalized through the abstract language of philosophers had indeed been constructed, but only by ignoring what the seventeenth century had not ignored, variation and diversity in taste and beauty. Thus it was that in the seventeenth century one still thought in terms of schools and manners, but in the next of Art. It was a complete reversal from the situation which had existed in the early eighteenth century, which was much more aware of historical relativism than was the end of the century—as may be gleaned from Voltaire, Du Bos, and also (as concerns taste) from the distinctions drawn by Roger de Piles in the last chapter of his little *Abrégé de la vie des peintres.* If the Rococo was the delightful style of sceptics and epicureans, of *mondains* and amateurs, the Neo-classic was the style of believers and *antiquomanes.* It was also the triumph in the fine arts of the philosophic spirit. This was remarked upon by Algarotti in 1756: "The philosophical spirit which has made such progress in our times and has penetrated all the domains of knowledge, has in a certain manner become the censor of the fine arts and particularly of architecture."[12] This spirit had begun with the censorship of the Rococo; it ended with the erection of the Neo-classic style, which fifty years later was an official style in France and the style of enlightened despotism in the rest of Europe.

NEITHER GOVERNMENT MEASURES, the definitions of philosophers, nor the doctrines of professors of the Academy could contain the forces which create art. Where, in the scheme we have outlined, did Fuseli, Blake, Prud'hon, or Flaxman fit? Taste could not be legislated, artists would not be turned out *en série,* and art, despite a rational aesthetic, could not escape history and imagination. The Neo-classic style and doctrine was no sooner crystallized than it began to alter, sprout heresies, and dissipate itself. The discovery of the past and its authority proved to be Pandora's box. For Winckelmann and David, indeed for many of their generation, there had been only one past worthy of artistic imitation and moral emulation: the Graeco-Roman past. Horace Walpole might write Gothic novels and build Strawberry Hill in a Medieval style—it was a private amusement. Yet these private whims proved to be portents of things to come, and while the very triumph of the Antique seemed assured, other pasts began to catch up with the artists trained to respect only one. Ossian made them think of the North, as did Madame de Staël's book on Germany. In 1799 Novalis wrote an essay on Christendom which began: "Those were beautiful and brilliant times, when Europe was a Christian land. . . ." Napoleon's expedition to Egypt proved to have important artistic consequences; Chateaubriand's *Génie du Christianisme* evoked a Christian heritage as valid and rich in artistic and literary motifs as the pagan past. Then, too, consider historical events: the French Revolution—that hope for a rebirth—turned into a nightmare and the epic of Napoleon provoked wars of liberation; these events brought forth heroes who hardly needed to be painted *à l'antique* in order to gain prestige. Thus, as Delacroix later saw, the Neo-classic with its universal pretensions, turned out after all merely to have been the fashion of the later eighteenth century. Yet it did not die, for the sentiment which had given it birth did not pass—it changed, and with it, form, too. One knew that something had been lost:

"Tot ist nun die Jugendliche Welt,"

wrote Hölderlin, and the great expectations of pre-1798 gave way to a sense of loss. The heroes of Plutarch made room once more for Ovid and Sappho, while the rhetorical gestures of the Horatii now turned into a voluptuous, languorous, and abandoned grace. The virtue of Roman matrons, the innocence of youthful Athenian and Corinthian maids were metamorphosed into the unattainable beauty of a Pauline Borghèse, Madame Récamier, and Prud'hon's Josephine. Energy turned to aestheticism and a world of manly heroes into one of dandies taking pleasure in a yearning for an unattainable beauty and a lost world. The world had lost its innocence,

"Was wir lieben, ist ein Schatten nur."

1. Concerning the Neo-classic and the past, see John Summerson, *Architecture in Britain 1530–1830* (Harmondsworth, Middlesex, 1953), p. 247: " 'Neo-classicism' is here used to describe that new spirit which, about the middle of the eighteenth century, altered the balance of the European's attitude to the past and therefore to the present and future." See also the excellent work of Louis Hautecoeur, *Histoire de l'architecture classique en France*, IV (Paris, 1952), especially pp. 16-69. A more intellectual approach is given by Pierre Francastel in his chapter on "Le Néo-Classique" in the Larousse series *L'Art et l'Homme*, ed. René Huyghe, III (Paris, 1957): "When one speaks of a return to the Antique, one usually sets the eighteenth century

within the cycle of the Renaissance. It is high time to explore it as a revolutionary century. Not only is it the century of Academies, but also that of History. It is not its boudoirs and its technique of beauty which keep it alive; but its discovery of the historical, which does not imply a return to the norms of purity, but a differential view of history" (p. 268). While it may be possible for us to see certain aspects of eighteenth-century thought as revolutionary, it may also be stressed that the implications of such thought often escaped the thinkers. It is extremely important to limit the meaning of the words used by the men of the past, and one may legitimately wonder whether, despite this awareness of the past, the eighteenth century really discovered historical thinking as this has come to be understood since the end of the nineteenth century. On the whole we are inclined to think that the Neo-classic, while inspired by the past and made possible by a better knowledge of it, was also in a certain sense an attempt to escape history. Return to the past implies less a sense of historical movement than the hope that somehow time may be countered.

2. On the number of eighteenth centuries see Roland Mortier's essay, "Unité ou scission du siècle des lumières?" in the Transactions of the First International Congress on the Enlightenment, *Studies on Voltaire and the Eighteenth Century*, XXVI (1963), 1207–1221; also, in the same group and series, Janine Buenzod, "De *l'Aufklärung* au *Sturm und Drang:* continuité ou rupture?" XXIV (1963), 289-313; and for a discussion of the English Enlightenment, Robert Voitle, "The Reason of the English Enlightenment," XXVII (1963), 1735 1774.

3. In his important *Réflexions sur l'imitation des artistes Grecs dans la peinture et dans la sculpture*, first published in German in 1755, Winckelmann wrote: "The temperature of a pure, serene, and moderate atmosphere undoubtedly had a great influence upon the physical constitution of the Greeks; and the manly exercises they were accustomed to since their youth ended by giving them a noble and elegant form." Quoted from the *Recueil de différentes pièces sur les arts*, trans. by Huber (Paris, 1785), p. 5. It is interesting to note how different this attitude is from that of Fontenelle who in the late seventeenth century posed this same question of climatic influence: he shows much more scepticism than the enthusiastic Winckelmann. Fontenelle was inclined to put more stress on human institutions and history in order to explain differences between Ancients and Moderns. But by the end of the century one was inclined to think of the Greeks much as one did about the noble savage, and the savages drawn for the illustrations of the voyages of Cook or Bougainville looked remarkably Greek.

4. The moral revival was given exemplary form by the personal action and life of Rousseau, citizen of Geneva. When Rousseau found success in letters he reformed himself and first began this reform through that of his dress: "I commenced my self-reform by my apparel; I abandoned gold braid and silk stockings, I took a simple round wig, left my sword, sold my watch, telling myself with unbelievable joy: thanks to heaven I shall no longer need to know the time." This was his way of quitting the Rococo style insofar as dress was concerned. It is noteworthy too that by a reform of 1775 for the students of the Academy in Rome, the students were enjoined to be sober, simple, and virtuous in their dress as well as their person. The call for virtue, however, goes back some time earlier. Rousseau's *First Discourse* dates from 1749. Montesquieu's *Esprit des lois*, in which virtue is equated with the republican form of government, dates from 1748.

5. For the satire directed against the Rococo style in architecture and ornament, see Cochin's *Recueil de quelques pièces concernant les arts* (Paris, 1757); these pieces were published in the then-influential *Mercure de France*. In the sixties Diderot was one of the writers who would

7

call for virtue among artists and for moral paintings. In fact this call can be traced to his first writings prompted by the Salons: it took the form of a demand for a return to great painting, to history, and a critique of the current style, of frivolity. The painters of the mid-eighteenth century were unfavorably compared to those of the *Grand Siècle*; it is only later on that he would turn to the Greeks for inspiration.

6. On Laugier see the section devoted to him by Hautecoeur, p. 54 ff.

7. See Francastel's chapter of *L'Art et l'Homme*, III, 267-268, for a list of titles.

8. These works of Piranesi appeared throughout this period: *Prima parte di architettura*, 1743; *Antichita Romane*, 1748; *Carceri*, 1750; *Della magnificenza ed architettura de Romani*, 1761; *Parere su l'architettura*, 1765.

9. E.g.: "The taste of the public contributed a great deal to the decadence of art; ephemeral and brilliant productions were received with acclamation; the attractions of wealth and facility of execution carried the artists along. The taste for drawing and for the Antique was decried and the following of principles regarded as servitude." In *Discours sur l'Origine, le Progrès et l'Etat actuel de la Peinture en France, Contenant des Notices sur les principaux Artistes de l'Académie; pour servir d'introduction au Salon* (Paris, 1785), p. 8. This is an anonymous pamphlet.

10. The art produced by the Academy under Lebrun is often referred to as an official art. It is quite true that this Academy had at that time a doctrine of art which might be regarded as official. However, *le Grand Goût* was not necessarily an official art or taste. It was derived from sources outside France and was merely that taste befitting monarchy; it was not exclusive of other tastes, though it was at the summit of the artistic hierarchy. The thought which informed this taste, patronage, and art was essentially artistic, and the result of the taste not only of patrons, but also of artists. The grand manner had been formed by individual artists. The aim of this art and doctrine was to glorify and immortalize the monarch; it was magnificence. But under the directorship of the Comte d'Angivilliers, in the 1770's, art became something else. D'Angivilliers encouraged the painting of history, but history itself had changed, as had artistic thought, so that the resulting art was quite different from that of the seventeenth century. When Van der Meulen, Martin des Batailles, or Joseph Parrocel painted battles in the seventeenth century, they celebrated Louis XIV, and when Lebrun painted his colossal Alexander series he was flattering Louis. But by the 1770's the very concept of the State had changed: it had become more impersonal, more of a machine, more aware of history and of the importance of the nation. Thus the concept of the subject of a king eventually gave way to that of the citizen. It is for this reason that history painting comes to be a species of moral lesson in civic virtue. This painting could draw its material from the Roman past but also the national past. This new type of history painting took into account, however unconsciously, this wider concept of the State which now included the citizen and the idea of the nation.

But there is another respect in which this art seems more official than ever before, namely in the proliferation of Academies in all of Europe. On this see Nikolaus Pevsner, *Academies of Art Past and Present* (Cambridge, England, 1940), especially ch. 4.

11. For more on the relation of the Neo-classic to history, see my essays, "Goût et civilisation" in *Revue d'Esthétique*, XV (January-March 1962), 30-42, and "Le Passé, le goût, et l'histoire" in *Studies on Voltaire and the Eighteenth Century*, Transactions . . ., XXVII (1963), 1445–1455.

12. Quoted by Hautecoeur, IV, 54.

The Neo-classic Style

Henry Hawley

THE NEO-CLASSIC STYLE derived its artistic ideas and motifs primarily from two sources —the Graeco-Roman past and the classicizing tradition which had existed in Western art since the Renaissance.

The renewed interest in the ancient world which can be discerned in the first half of the eighteenth century was symptomatic of the spirit which was to give birth to Neo-classicism after 1750. The most famous and dramatic evidence of that interest was the excavations of the ancient cities of Herculaneum and Pompeii, which were begun in 1738 and 1763 respectively. Of equal importance was the dissemination of knowledge about the ancient world through the publication of illustrated books, beginning with *Antiquité expliquée* of Bernard Montfaucon of 1719. Some of these books, such as Robert Wood's *Ruins of Palmyra* of 1753 and his *Ruins of Balbec* of 1757, constituted additions to knowledge, since they provided illustrations of seldom-visited sites. Even the remains of ancient Greece were for most Europeans largely legendary until given concrete form in LeRoy's *Les Ruines des plus beaux monuments de la Grèce* of 1758 and Stuart and Revett's *The Antiquities of Athens* of 1762, 1789, and 1795. Piranesi performed a similar function for the ruins of Italy. The collecting of ancient art, while hardly a new phenomenon, also contributed to artistic life in the second half of the eighteenth century. Often collectors of antiquities were patrons of innovators in painting and architecture. Cardinal Albani, for whom Mengs painted his *Parnassus*, is a famous example. Many artists functioned as dealers in antiquities. The English gentlemen who visited Rome after 1755 often returned home with ancient sculpture sold to them by the painter Gavin Hamilton. His pictures were commissioned largely by persons to whom he had first sold antiquities. During the thirty years before Canova's arrival in Rome, the sculptors of that city were concerned almost entirely with the restoration and copying of ancient marbles, producing few works of their own invention. Thus excavation, publication, and collecting, each in its own way, demonstrated the renewed interest in the Graeco-Roman past and contributed to the contemporary Neo-classic style.

Of still greater importance for the genesis of Neo-classicism was the classicizing tradition in Western art which had begun in the Renaissance. Raphael was considered by men of the

eighteenth century to be the greatest exponent of the tradition. From him it descended through the Carracci to their Bolognese followers. At the end of the seventeenth century, Maratti was the most famous Roman practitioner in that tradition. In the eighteenth century Batoni augmented Bolognese classicism with direct quotations from Graeco-Roman art, thus preparing it to be of primary influence upon such early Neo-classic masters as Mengs. The Italian tradition of Raphael and the Carracci had produced an important offshoot in the seventeenth century in the person of the great French painter Nicolas Poussin, who had been active in Rome and many of whose works remained there in the eighteenth century. Poussin influenced the beginnings of Neo-classicism in two ways. First, his work and that of his French followers, particularly Le Brun, determined the style of early French Neo-classic painters, such as Restout and Lagrenée. Their work is the product of a conscious attempt on the part of the French royal administration, after about 1750, to impose upon contemporary artists the ideals of French academic painting of the last half of the seventeenth century. More direct and significant for the future of Neo-classicism was the example offered by Poussin's sober, carefully designed compositions, his serious subject matter, and his informed use of archaeologically inspired details of architecture, costume, and household furnishings. First Gavin Hamilton, and later David, were inspired by these elements of Poussin's style.

An older European tradition was of great importance, too, for the beginnings of the Neo-classic style in architecture. The late Renaissance architect Palladio, together with his Roman literary mentor Vitruvius, had become widely admired and imitated, especially in England, but also in France and Northern Italy, during the first half of the eighteenth century. Following the leadership of the gifted amateur architect Lord Burlington, Palladianism became the standard of English architectural taste long before 1750. Though the Palladians employed the vocabulary of ancient architecture with what they felt to be great purity and correctness, their aim was to equal the beauty of Graeco-Roman architecture, not to copy it literally and in its totality. However, the buildings of Burlington and his followers often resembled ancient structures. The already established Palladian taste probably contributed significantly to the quick acceptance in England of the early Neo-classic style when it was imported from Italy by Adam.

In seventeenth-century France, the architecture of the Italian Renaissance had been adapted by François Mansart, Lemercier, Le Vau, J. H. Mansart, and others to French taste and customs, producing thereby a distinctive national architectural tradition of classical predisposition which had persisted, at least in so far as external architectural design was concerned, into the mid-eighteenth century. Beginning about 1690, successive modifications had resulted in the delicate, curvilinear, asymmetrical style of interior architecture and decoration which we call the Rococo. In the decade of the 1750's the same official critics who imposed in France a return to the style of academic seventeenth-century painting agitated for a return to the severer style of interior architecture and furnishings which had been popular about 1700. They met with limited success. More important for the future were the, at first, small number of private patrons who, in the same decade, employed designers to create for them interiors which displayed the vocabulary of decorative motifs of early Neo-classicism. From these beginnings

10

developed the mature Louis XVI style which, though sharing motifs which had originated in the international Roman art world, was clearly French in spirit. As in England, early Neo-classicism in France demanded few modifications of the tradition of external architecture.

Evidence about the development of the early Neo-classic architectural style in Italy is both less abundant (in part because little was actually constructed) and less well studied than in England and France, but it is clear that a similar pattern of development existed there.

(The importance of Rome as a center of artistic creativity in the eighteenth century has already been alluded to. Rather surprisingly, that city witnessed the birth of Neo-classicism and remained the primary source of new stylistic concepts during most of the last half of the century) Rome had occupied a similar position in the seventeenth century, but before the beginning of the eighteenth century leadership had passed to Paris. The reasons for its return to Rome are not entirely clear. Historically, centers of artistic innovation have tended to spring up where generous patronage was to be found, but local patronage in Rome was rather meager in the eighteenth century. Several less obvious inducements brought artists to live there. Since the sixteenth century it had been customary for artists to go to Rome, if possible, to complete their training by experiencing Italian art at first-hand. In the middle of the eighteenth century, by far the most important and extensive collections of ancient art were to be found in Rome or nearby. Thus, Rome was the natural center for the study of ancient and modern Italian art, both of which, as has already been mentioned, were of great importance in the formation of the Neo-classic style. Finally, such personal reasons as cheap living conditions, a pleasant climate, and a sympathetic artistic milieu must have induced some artists to reside there.

The only center which rivaled Rome at this time as a source of stylistic influence was Paris. The well-deserved reputation of France for high quality of craftsmanship and design in interior architecture and furnishings resulted in continued dependence upon her authority in those fields by Germany, Scandinavia, and Russia throughout the eighteenth century. The number and talent of French architects caused their frequent employment outside their native land. French painting was also popular in other European countries, but until David achieved his maturity as an artist in the 1780's, major stylistic innovations were not produced in Paris. Her leadership—clearly re-established after the Revolution and strengthened during the period of Napoleon's domination of Europe—lasted into our own times.

NEO-CLASSIC PAINTING can be roughly divided into two successive stylistic phases. The earlier has been called the Neo-classic style; the later, Romantic Neo-classicism.

The Neo-classic style in painting emerged directly from the Italian late Baroque classicizing tradition. Batoni, perhaps more than any other single artist, provided the necessary link between the Bolognese tradition and Neo-classicism. His influence, as well as that of such of his contemporaries as Corvi and Benefial, was strongly felt by the generation of Italian painters which followed. By the 1740's, Batoni had firmly established his Roman reputation as a painter. In that decade Hamilton first came to Rome. Piranesi and Clérisseau, Mengs and

Vien were also there, but Neo-classicism seems to have coalesced as a style only in the next decade.

In 1749 an event of importance for French art occurred. It had been decided that the brother of Mme. de Pompadour, the future Marquis de Marigny, was to become Surintendent des Bâtiments du Roi, a position which carried with it a potential for enormous influence upon French art. In order to prepare him for his future duties, Marigny set out in that year on a tour of Italy. He was accompanied by the architect Soufflot, the draughtsman Cochin, and the polemicist against the Rococo, the Abbé Le Blanc. This journey did not immediately either alter Marigny's personal taste, which was typical of his time, nor divert the stylistic stream of French art, but the choice of Marigny's traveling companions indicates that persons of influence at court desired change. Marigny himself was prepared by the experience to accept a new style when the time was ripe. During the last half of the eighteenth century, French art, nevertheless, remained somewhat *retardataire* in comparison to that of Rome or even London, perhaps because the machinery of state patronage on the lower levels remained in the hands of older, more conservative artists.

The Neo-classic style in painting seems to have crystallized in Rome toward the end of the decade of the 1750's. In 1755 Winckelmann, the chief theoretician of Neo-classicism, arrived in Rome. At about the same time, Hamilton returned from a stay in England and shortly thereafter began his series of Poussinesque compositions which constitute the first recognizably Neo-classic pictures. Mengs associated himself with Winckelmann shortly after the latter's arrival in Rome. To Mengs goes the honor of having produced the manifesto of Neo-classicism, his *Parnassus* in the Villa Albani. It was painted in 1761, and its accessibility, in a house already famed as a center of antiquarian research, imparted to it the function of a public declaration. However, the stylistic innovations introduced by Hamilton at approximately the same date were destined to be of far greater significance for the future than any contribution of Mengs. In Hamilton's pictures, the space occupied by the major figures is confined to a narrow band near the front of the picture plane. The figures are arranged in a frieze-like composition within that limited space. The design of particular figures becomes hard and precise. In his choice of subject matter, too, Hamilton was an innovator. He rejected the pleasing, often erotic subjects of the late Baroque for ones drawn from classical mythology and history which illustrated moral principles or heroic actions.

It was a young artist from Pennsylvania, Benjamin West, who was the first to be profoundly influenced by Hamilton's innovations. West was in Rome from 1760 to 1763. Especially in his early works he followed very closely the style established by Hamilton. On leaving Italy he went to London, where he won the favor of George III. West's success lent prestige to the style which he practiced, and it quickly gained popularity in England. The arrival in London in 1766 of Angelica Kauffmann, who had been in Rome and had adapted early Neo-classicism to her own very feminine talent, reinforced public acceptance of the new style in England.

In France the beginnings of Neo-classic painting can be traced to the exhibition in the Salon of 1761 of a picture by Vien which paraphrased the subject and composition of an ancient Roman fresco. However, the style practiced by Vien in his early works had far more to do with the traditions of French academic painting than with Hamilton's innovations, and his subjects, though antique, reflected a Rococo taste for pleasing eroticism. As early as 1755 Greuze had won acclaim from Diderot for his scenes of peasant life which included, almost incidentally, moralizing sentiments. In style, Greuze's pictures—especially those of the later 1760's—have more in common with Roman Neo-classicism than do Vien's. The future, however, lay with Vien. About 1770 the great series of decorations, now in the Frick Collection, which Fragonard had prepared for du Barry's pavilion at Louveciennes were rejected, and Vien was commissioned to paint substitutes. Neo-classicism was thereby given official sanction by the highest court circles.

More important than any of his own works was Vien's role as the teacher of the young Jacques Louis David, who entered his studio in 1765. In 1774 David won the *Prix de Rome*. The following year he went with Vien to Rome, remaining there until 1781. By that date, David was moving close to the style of his early maturity. In Rome he not only learned the rudiments of Neo-classicism, but also added Caravaggesque lighting effects to his style. In 1784 he returned to Rome to produce *The Oath of the Horatii*, which has been recognized as the definitive statement of the first phase of Neo-classicism. It was exhibited, first in Rome, and then in Paris, in 1785. In both cities it won immediate acclaim. David assumed the position of leadership in French painting which he was to hold for thirty years. In *The Oath of the Horatii* David carried to their farthest limits the implications of Hamilton's stylistic innovations. The result was a style of painting which approaches colored bas-reliefs. In the settings and accessories of his pictures, David made use of the best current information on ancient Roman civilization in order to impart an air of verisimilitude to his work. Like Hamilton, David chose serious subjects for his pictures, but, in addition, he chose subjects which had immediate social and political reference in a France fast approaching the Revolution. The contemporary significance of their subjects is probably the characteristic of these pictures of David's early maturity which gives to them, despite their cold and precise style, a vigor and even passion which remain intuitively understandable today.

The second phase of the Neo-classic style in painting is characterized, in its most extreme manifestations, by a reduction of the feigned volume of figures to linear silhouettes and the elimination of the representation of space through the use of linear perspective. Greek vase painting, which came to be widely known and admired in the second half of the eighteenth century, was the primary source of this stylistic development. The use of pure outline, without shading to indicate volume, is to be found first in late eighteenth-century published illustrations of vase paintings. Also significant was Gothic art, particularly Italian painting before the fifteenth century. Accompanying these formal innovations was a new spectrum of subject matter. The ideal and heroic themes which had been valued from Hamilton to David were frequently exchanged for ones emphasizing the emotional states of particular individuals. Artists again attempted to convey pictorially emotions, such as love, fear, anger, and hate, experienced by individuals, often within the context of unusual situations. The Graeco-Roman past remained, for a time, the setting generally chosen by painters for the scenes which they wished to depict, but gradually they came to use other locales, also removed in time and sometimes in space from their own world. Christian themes once more were employed by some painters. It is because of this shift to personally relevant subjects that this second stylistic phase has sometimes been termed Romantic Neo-classicism.

The originator of this second phase remains uncertain. Henry Fuseli probably contributed much. His youth in Zürich was spent in the midst of one of the most advanced proto-Romantic literary circles to be found anywhere in Europe at the time. Fuseli's father was a painter; thus, he became acquainted at an early age with the artist's profession. However, he was well into his twenties before he made a final choice between an artistic or a literary career. In 1764, after a stay in Berlin, Fuseli went to London. There he met Reynolds, who encouraged the young artist to take up painting. He had previously confined himself to drawing, and he was never to achieve the technical competence in painting which was his as a draughtsman. During this first stay in London Fuseli met, and perhaps influenced, two young English artists, Blake and Flaxman, both of whom were destined to play a large part in Romantic Neo-classicism— Blake by virtue of his own work, which went largely unappreciated during his lifetime, and Flaxman because of his influence upon Continental artists who reached maturity about 1800, particularly the young Ingres. In 1770 Fuseli went to Italy where he remained for eight years. The impact of his style upon the contemporary Roman artistic world is uncertain, though he is known to have influenced the Swedish sculptor Sergel with whom he became acquainted there. Fuseli returned to England in 1779. He remained an active and, in his role of professor at the Academy, influential artist in London until his death in 1825. Flaxman, in his turn, was in Italy from 1787 until 1794. A somewhat restrained version of the linear phase of Neo-classicism manifested itself among younger Italian artists—Appiani, Canova, Giani—during the last two decades of the eighteenth century, but whether this was an indigenous development or the product of northern influence remains unclear. The Italian artistic milieu does seem to have been the source of the Romantic Neo-classic style developed by German and Scandinavian artists such as Abildgaard and Carstens.

Perhaps because of the immense prestige of the works of David's early maturity, the second phase of the Neo-classic style in painting did not reach France until close to 1800. In that year David himself exhibited *The Rape of the Sabines*, in which, for him, a new emphasis upon linear design is evident. Similar tendencies were already at play in the work of some of his pupils, for example Girodet. A degree of interest in personal, anti-heroic subjects had persisted in France through the years of David's artistic domination, particularly in the work of Prud'hon. The new linearism, often combined with highly subjective content, found its outstanding French exponent in another pupil of David, Jean Auguste Dominique Ingres. From Ingres descended the long line of French classicistic painters of the nineteenth century. In the work of Ingres' followers, elements of the Neo-classic style lingered on, but they were employed in a constantly more doctrinaire manner and became, therefore, less suitable as vehicles for the expression of individual artistic intent.

SINCE THE RENAISSANCE, European sculpture had been based upon the example of the antique. For that reason the Neo-classic style in sculpture was less obviously revolutionary than in painting, and its manifestations are, therefore, sometimes more difficult to recognize. Its basic characteristics can, however, be defined. Contrapposto was abandoned. For the twisting forms of Baroque sculpture which delimited space was substituted an emphasis upon elegance of line created by mass seen in silhouette. Gone, too, was the realism of surface textures which had typified the work of Bernini and those whom he influenced. It was replaced by a more neutral surface treatment which did not seek to attract attention to itself.

In sculpture, as in painting, Gavin Hamilton appears to have played a major role in the introduction of the Neo-classic style. In the decades of the 60's and 70's he helped to mold the artistic personalities of the English sculptors Nollekens and Banks. More important was his influence upon the greatest of the practitioners of the Neo-classic style in sculpture, Canova. When Canova came to Rome in 1779 he brought with him from Venice a late Baroque manner which he had already made his own. However, he soon dropped all traces of the Baroque and adapted Hamilton's method of figure composition to sculpture. In this way Canova developed a style which was to serve as the point of departure for Neo-classic sculpture for more than fifty years. A concealed but disturbing erotic undercurrent, combined with the refined linearism which is observable particularly in his reliefs and drawings, serves to link Canova's style with that of the Romantic Neo-classicists. Canova won for himself an enormous European reputation during his lifetime. His most famous pupil, Thorvaldsen, is only one example of his widespread influence.

Canova's influence was, however, not so quickly felt in France. There sculpture was dominated, until after the Revolution, by a style which has been described as bourgeois realism and is best exemplified in the work of Houdon. In its simplicity of figure composition, this style parallels that of Canova, but it lacks his somewhat mannered elegance of line. Clodion, in his intimate sculptures, incorporated classically-inspired motifs, but, like Houdon, he failed to assume the Neo-classic style in its entirety, retaining in his choice of subjects a link with the Rococo. It was only after the Revolution that Canovian Neo-classicism manifested itself in France in the work of sculptors such as Chaudet. Thereafter, so long as the Neo-classic style persisted in sculpture, the influence of Canova cannot be overlooked.

THE NEO-CLASSIC STYLE in architecture and articles of household use seems to have followed a more consistent pattern of development than in painting. At first, the Neo-classic style was characterized by the application of decorative motifs, often directly copied from ancient sources, to buildings and objects which retained their traditional forms. At a somewhat later time, structure, as well as ornament, became imitative of Graeco-Roman examples.

Since Winckelmann had championed it, Greek art had been widely considered both earlier than and superior to Roman art. However, in mid-eighteenth-century Europe, Greek art was

15

little known; it was, therefore, Roman architecture which was initially important as a source for Neo-classicism. Several decades were needed for the accumulation of sufficient knowledge of Greek architecture to permit its widespread imitation. As early as the 1770's some architects of advanced taste, conspicuously Ledoux in France and Stuart and Revett in England, had displayed prominently elements drawn from Greek architecture in their designs. In doing so, they were perhaps inspired by the French theoretician of architecture, Laugier.

However, toward the end of the eighteenth century, the choice of ancient modes to be imitated came to be determined primarily by the associative values which they possessed. An admiration for the whole of Greek culture resulted in the widespread adoption of her architectural style in England, Germany, and Scandinavia, but in Italy and France, ancient Rome continued to be the chief source of stylistic inspiration. Italy's allegiance to Roman precedent is easily explained by her occupancy of the same territory as the ancient state, and hence her sentimental identification with its culture. Interestingly enough, imitation of Greek architecture seems to have occurred earlier and more frequently in southern Italy and Sicily, where ancient Greek colonies had existed, than in other parts of the peninsula. Even before the Revolution, David had held up to French society the example of republican Rome as a political system worthy of emulation. When Napoleon assumed dictatorial powers, he made use of this already established concept of the identification of contemporary and ancient political institutions, pushed forward in time the ancient precedent to be followed, and assumed for his regime the panoply of grandeur that had been imperial Rome's. It was only after the Bourbon restoration that building in the Greek style became customary in France.

Again one must turn to Italy in order to observe the beginnings of the Neo-classic style in architecture. The ancient remains which were to be found there contributed significantly to the birth of Neo-classic architecture. Since the earliest manifestation of the new style is to be found in the application of archaeologically derived decorative details to interior architecture and furnishings, the excavations at Herculaneum and Pompeii were especially useful because they made available many examples of comparable features of ancient Roman domestic life. The new interest in the past appears in the second quarter of the century in the very popular views of ruins produced by Panini. Even more important were the designs of Piranesi. He first came to Rome in the 1740's, and by the end of the decade he had taken up permanent residence there. He remained in Rome until his death in 1778. In contrast to Panini's work, Piranesi's not only makes use of ancient ruins for the pleasingly picturesque subjects which they provide for pictorial representation but also reflects the intense intellectual interest of their author in Roman architecture. Therefore, Piranesi's prints offered, along with their high intrinsic value as works of art, faithfully reproduced details of ornament which were useful to other designers. Though literary evidence is at the present time largely lacking, it seems likely that Piranesi also exerted considerable influence upon the architecture of both England and France through his personal contact with students from those lands who were studying in Rome.

Among the visual recorders of ancient remains who were active in Rome was a young French draughtsman and architect, Charles Louis Clérisseau. He came to Rome in 1749 and worked at the French Academy there until 1753. He was on his way home when he met Robert Adam in Florence. Adam persuaded Clérisseau to become his teacher of architectural drawing and to help him in his investigations of ancient ruins. To this end, Clérisseau accompanied Adam to Dalmatia where they made illustrations of the Palace of Diocletian at Spalatro, which Adam later published. Through Clérisseau and Piranesi, Adam was initiated into the cult of archaeology which permeated contemporary Roman artistic circles. After his return to England in 1759, Adam precipitated a stylistic revolution there by applying his newly acquired knowledge of ancient architecture to the planning and decoration of domestic interiors.

Adam's chief rival in England was his slightly older contemporary, William Chambers, whose career demonstrates another important aspect of the development of the Neo-classic style. Though Chambers visited Italy in the early 1750's, the primary source of his architectural style was France, where he studied under Blondel and became acquainted with the major French architects of his generation. The classicizing tradition of seventeenth-century French architecture had been reinforced in the first half of the eighteenth century by J. N. Servandoni (a pupil of Panini) who, in 1733, had designed the façade of St. Sulpice in Paris. On the basis of the tasteful classicizing manner which he had learned in Paris and the parallel tradition which prevailed in England, Chambers constructed his personal architectural style. Classical decorative motifs of an archaeological character were employed by Chambers, but their principal source seems to have been not the direct inspiration of ancient remains or contemporary Roman practice, but rather the products of those sources as sifted through French taste. From about 1755 until the Revolution, architectural ideas were freely exchanged among England, France, and Italy. It is often impossible to give, with complete assurance, credit for innovations of style to individuals or even to national schools.

One of the most interesting architects of the generation following Chambers and Adam was George Dance the Younger. He went to Italy about 1758 and remained there for five years. Dance built little, and several of his most important works have not survived; but, as we know it, his architectural style was more advanced than that of either Chambers or Adam. Dance abandoned the Palladian elements which had persisted in the designs of his older contemporaries. Shortly after 1800 he participated in the second phase of the Neo-classic style in architecture through his use of a purely Greek Doric portico in a country house design. Dance exerted great influence upon the next generation of English architects, particularly Soane.

The beginnings of the influence of Greek sources upon English architecture can be found in the works of James Stuart and Nicholas Revett, the authors of *The Antiquities of Athens*, which appeared in 1762, 1789, and 1795. As early as 1758 Stuart built a garden ornament in the form of a Greek Doric temple, and both men employed architectural elements of Greek derivation in their designs of the 60's and 70's, but it was not until close to the end of the century that Greek motifs began to play a dominant role in English architecture. In this development, the influence of a few advanced French architects, for example Ledoux, cannot be neglected. In the nineteenth century, the Neo-classic style was challenged by the increasingly popular Gothic revival.

17

The history of the Neo-classic style in English furniture and decorations followed a course parallel to that in architecture. Adam is almost as famous as a designer of household accoutrement as he is as an architect. It was he who popularized the use of archaeologically derived motifs in the design of every conceivable useful object. In that realm the stylistic revolution which he incited was even more dramatic than in architecture, since it was in the design of household furnishings that the French Rococo style had exercised its strongest influence in England, producing the local variant which we call today the "Chippendale" style in furniture. Among the best known of the imitators of the Adam manner was Hepplewhite, whose designs for furniture were widely used. French influence did not entirely disappear in England with the passing of the Rococo. It can be observed in Holland's architectural and furniture designs and in the early published furniture designs of Sheraton.

An archaeologically inspired approach to form, as well as to decoration, can be found first in England in the ceramics produced by the Wedgwood firm as early as the 1770's. A well-known example is their copy of the famous Roman glass vase, known as the Portland vase. Wedgwood's ceramics enjoyed wide influence and popularity on the Continent, as well as in England. Imitations of ancient furniture forms were first introduced in England by a wealthy amateur, Thomas Hope, toward 1800. Hope displayed considerable originality, but he followed, to a degree, the style of Napoleon's chief architects and decorators, Percier and Fontaine.

Although French architecture followed a stylistic progression similar to that of England during the last half of the eighteenth century, the attendant circumstances were quite different. In France there were no dominant architectural personalities of the stature of a Chambers or Adam. That is not to say that French architects were less talented than the English. But perhaps because of diverse, competitive, and sophisticated patronage, no architect emerged as a decisive leader of taste.

The oldest, and first, of the architects working in the Neo-classic style in France was Soufflot. In 1749 he had accompanied the Marquis de Marigny, the brother of Pompadour and intended Surintendent des Bâtiments, to Italy. As a result of the acquaintance thus established, Soufflot, in 1756, was awarded the commission for the most important building constructed in France in the last half of the eighteenth century, the Church of Ste.-Geneviève, later the Pantheon. In the design of this building Soufflot was strongly influenced by Roman architecture, though Renaissance sources are also evident, most obviously in the dome, which is ultimately dependent upon Michelangelo's design for the dome of St. Peter's. Until his death in 1780 Soufflot continued to simplify and refine his initial concept of Ste.-Geneviève. The result is a structure of great sobriety, built with astonishing virtuosity of construction in stone.

Among Soufflot's contemporaries, mention must first be made of Ange-Jacques Gabriel, who served as Premier Architecte du Roi from 1742 to 1775. Gabriel's taste was not particularly advanced and he made no stylistic innovations, but, under his direction and with the help of younger collaborators, several distinguished royal works were carried out between 1750 and 1775. Among them were the twin buildings which are the architectural ornaments of the Place de la Concorde. In style they have more to do with the classicizing tradition of the seventeenth century than with Neo-classicism. In 1763 Gabriel began the Petit Trianon for Mme. de Pompadour. Early Neo-classicism is expressed most clearly in the design of some of its interiors, which were not executed until near the end of the decade, after Pompadour's death. Gabriel's last important project was the Opera at Versailles, which was completed in the spring of 1770, in time for the festivities attending the marriage of the future Louis XVI and Marie-Antoinette.

Some of the talented younger contemporaries of Soufflot and Gabriel should be cited. Etienne-Louis Boullée was one of the most advanced architects of his day. Unfortunately, few of his executed works survive. Richard Mique first assisted, then succeeded, Gabriel as Premier Architecte. He was the favorite architect of Marie-Antoinette and executed for her exquisite interiors and small pleasure pavilions at Versailles and elsewhere. Claude-Nicolas Ledoux's early career was devoted to private houses, most notably the pavilion of Louveciennes for Mme. du Barry. In his later executed and published works he carried to its furthest extent a tendency toward geometric simplification which constitutes one facet of the Neo-classic style in architecture. He may also be credited with originating the organic concept of city planning. The following list of names of architects active in the last half of the eighteenth century who produced buildings of considerable distinction is, although incomplete, indicative of the abundance of contemporary French architectural talent: Chalgrin, de Wailly, Gondoin, J.-D. Antoine, Victor Louis, Bélanger.

In contrast to England, where the early Neo-classic style in household furnishings was introduced by Adam, the style seems, as it were, to have come in by the back door in France, and is thus difficult to trace. Perhaps primary credit should go to the great amateur of the arts, La Live de Jully, who, between 1755 and 1758, had his house redecorated by the architect Barreau, a disciple of Piranesi, and the painter Louis Le Lorrain, who seems to have been the more important contributor to the scheme. This early phase of Neo-classicism in French decoration is characterized by the use, in an abundance which recalls seventeenth-century taste, of rather heavy classical motifs. In the following decade the style was popularized through the printed designs of Delafosse, and his name has thus come to be associated with the taste, though there is no evidence that he originated it. Early Neo-classicism seems to have gained wide popularity in sophisticated Parisian circles in the 1760's, but the opening of Mme. du Barry's Pavillon de Louveciennes in 1771 gave to the style the stamp of approval of the court. A few years earlier, a more attenuated and refined version of the style had been suggested in some designs by Neufforge and Bélanger. That innovation was termed the *style étrusque*. In 1777 Bélanger designed for the Conte d'Artois, the king's brother, a pleasure house on the outskirts of Paris called Bagatelle. J.-J. Boileau provided designs for its decoration. Bagatelle served much the same function as Louveciennes, that of demonstrating the approval of the inner circle of the court of an already popular style, the *style étrusque*. In the next decade designers such as Lalonde and Dugourc further refined the *style étrusque* and, by introducing into the design of parts of furniture, such as legs or backs, forms based upon Graeco-Roman furniture, paved the way for post-Revolutionary styles of decoration. More important, however, was the furniture which David commissioned in the 1780's from the chairmaker Jacob to be used as studio props for his paintings. It was in these pieces that, for the first time, an attempt was made to accurately reproduce Roman furniture in its entirety. After the Revolution Napoleon's chief architects, Percier and Fontaine, expanded the vocabulary of furniture forms established by David and created a consistent style of interior architecture, adapted to contemporary needs, in which such furniture might be used. That style, based upon evidence provided by archaeology, quickly spread throughout Europe.

The Rococo persisted longer in Germany and Scandinavia than elsewhere in Europe. When the early Neo-classic style in architecture did arrive, it came from France, chiefly through the agency of younger architects forced to migrate by an oversupply of trained professionals in their homeland. Published designs and imported French furniture provided additional ingredients for the development of local versions of the early Neo-classic style of interior decoration in the countries of Northern Europe. It was only toward 1800 that important native architects appeared, particularly the German Schinkel and the Dane Hansen, and the style in which they worked was the mature Neo-classic, with strong reliance upon Greek sources. In interior decoration, the manner of Percier and Fontaine, often simplified, was much more readily accepted in Germany and Scandinavia than had been the early Neo-classic.

Although Neo-classic painting, sculpture, architecture, and household furnishings continued to be produced throughout Europe and in America in considerable quantity until about 1850, and sporadically thereafter, other stylistic revivals came to the fore. Forms and motifs of recognizably Neo-classic derivation persisted, but with the passage of time they became increasingly heavy, flaccid, and coarse. More important, by the second quarter of the nineteenth century Neo-classicism appears to have lost the intellectual vigor that inspired its earlier manifestations. It was perhaps the unseemly spectacle of its slow decline which contributed most to the adverse criticism so often heaped upon Neo-classicism in the twentieth century.

T HE FOLLOWING *short bibliography contains the principal sources used in writing the preceding essay. The bibliographies contained in these works include almost the entire literature of Neo-classicism:*

Friedlaender, Walter. *David to Delacroix.* Cambridge, Massachusetts, 1952.

Hautecoeur, Louis. *Histoire de l'architecture classique en France.* Vols. IV, V, VI. Paris, 1952–1955.

Hitchcock, Henry-Russell. *Architecture Nineteenth and Twentieth Centuries.* Harmondsworth, Middlesex, 1958.

Lavagnino, Emilio. *L'Arte Moderna.* Turin, 1961.

Locquin, Jean. *La peinture d'histoire en France de 1747 à 1785.* Paris, 1912.

Rosenblum, Robert. "The International Style of 1800: A Study in Linear Abstraction." Unpublished Ph.D. dissertation, New York University, 1956.

Summerson, John. *Architecture in Britain 1530–1830.* Harmondsworth, Middlesex, 1953.

Waterhouse, Ellis. *Painting in Britain 1530–1790.* Harmondsworth, Middlesex, 1953.

Watson, F. J. B. *Louis XVI Furniture.* London, 1960.

Zeitler, Rudolf. "Klassizismus und Utopia," *Figura*, no. 5 (1954).

The Catalogue

THE OBJECTS included in the catalogue which follows have been arranged according to an inexact method. Both chronological and geographical criteria have been employed. Whenever possible, an effort has been made to suggest stylistic relationships through juxtaposition. A short biographical note precedes the listing of works for which authorship can be determined. In those cases in which more than one work by a particular artist are included, they have been grouped together following the biographical sketch, despite the differences in style which are sometimes present as the result of evolution within a single *oeuvre*.

H. H.

Giovanni Paolo Panini

Piacenza ca.1692—Rome 1765/8

In 1715 Panini was still in Piacenza, but two years later he was studying in Rome with Locatelli and Luti. He was made a member of the Accademia di San Luca, and became its Princeps in 1754. In 1732 he was made a member of the French Royal Academy and also taught at its extension in Rome. Panini was famous primarily as a painter of ruins.

1 *The Colosseum and Other Monuments*

Oil on canvas, 39 x 53 inches. Signed and dated (on pedestal at left): I. P. Panini/Romae 1735.
Collection: The Duke of Norfolk, Beachill, Yorkshire.
Literature: Wilbur D. Peat, "Two Paintings of Roman Monuments by Panini," JHMA *Bulletin*, XXXVII (October 1950), 22-25. Richard Paul Wunder, "The Colosseum Series: A Glimpse into Panini's Stylistic Development," *The Art Quarterly*, XXI (Summer 1958), 160-165. Ferdinando Arisi, *Gian Paolo Panini* (Piacenza, 1961), p. 149, no. 102, fig. 153.

Pendant to the painting which follows, *The Pantheon and Other Monuments*. A similar composition by Panini, dated 1734, is in the Lawrence Art Museum, Williams College, Mass.

John Herron Museum of Art, Indianapolis

2 The Pantheon and Other Monuments

Signed and dated (on pedestal at left): I. P. Panini/
Romae 1735.
Collection: See preceding entry.
Literature: See preceding entry. Arisi, p. 149, no. 101, fig.
152.
A pendant to the painting which precedes, *The Colosseum
and Other Monuments.*

John Herron Museum of Art, Indianapolis

3 *Interior of an Art Gallery*

Water color, pen and ink, on paper, 17-3/8 x 27-3/8 inches.
Signed (on pedestal at left): I. P. Panini fecit. Painted
ca.1757.
Collections: M. A. Rateau; M. Edouard Moratello.
Related to a painting in the Metropolitan Museum, New
York (see Ferdinando Arisi, *Gian Paolo Panini* [Piacenza,
1961], no. 249) dated 1757. The Metropolitan Museum
painting is a replica of one, dated 1756, in the National
Gallery of Scotland, Edinburgh. A third version, dated
1758, is in the Louvre, Paris. Among the figures included
in the water color, it is the Duc de Choiseul who holds a
palette, while Panini examines a copy of the Aldobrandini
Wedding.

The Art Institute of Chicago
Gift of Mrs. Emily Crane Chadbourne

Giovanni Marchiori

Caviola di Agordo 1696—Treviso 1778

Marchiori received his earliest training in the studio of the Venetian sculptor in wood, Andrea Brustalon. He himself worked in that medium until about 1735. By the 1740's his work had become restrained in style, foreshadowing the Neo-classic. In 1765 he moved to Treviso where he remained until his death. His work was admired by Canova.

4 *Ideal Bust* (with pedestal)

Marble, 18-1/2 x 13-1/4 inches (pedestal carved, painted, and gilded wood). Inscribed (on diagonal strap): IOAN MARCHIORI.
Collection: English private collection.
Literature: D. Graeme Keith, "A Marble Bust by Giovanni Marchiori," RISD *Museum Notes*, XLIV (December 1957), 3-5, figs. 3,4.
The pedestal, which is probably the original, is a fine example of Italian late Baroque furniture.

Museum of Art, Rhode Island School of Design

Marco Benefial

5 *St. Margaret of Cortona Finds the Body of Her Lover*

Oil on canvas, 47-1/4 x 57-1/8 inches. Painted ca.1725–30.
Collections: Purchased from a Roman art dealer, 1956.
Exhibited: Rome, Palazzo delle Esposizioni, Il Settecento a Roma, 1959, no. 74.
Literature: "Marco Benefial: 'Storia di S. Margherita da Cortona'," *Bolletino d'Arte*, XLI (October-December 1956), 373–374.

Rome 1684—Rome 1764

Benefial was one of the most successful Roman painters of the generation before Batoni. As early as 1703 he had established himself as an independent master. During his long life he executed many easel pictures and frescos of both religious and secular subjects. The most famous of his pupils was Anton Raffael Mengs, who worked in his studio from 1741 to 1745.

A large sketch for one of two pictures of scenes from the life of St. Margaret of Cortona which Benefial painted for the Chiesa dell' Aracoeli in Rome.

Galleria Nazionale d'Arte Antica, Rome

Pompeo Batoni

Lucca 1708—Rome 1787

Of all the painters of his generation, Batoni carried Bolognese classicism closest to the Neo-classic style and influenced most young painters who developed it, particularly Mengs, but also Hamilton and David. By 1740 Batoni had won a position of leadership for himself among Roman painters which he held until near the end of his life. Among his early works history pictures dominate. Later he became famous as a portraitist, and in this capacity influenced many English painters of the late eighteenth century.

6 *The Triumph of Venice*

Oil on canvas, 68-5/8 x 112-5/8 inches. Painted in 1737.
Collections: Painted for Marco Foscarini, Venetian Am-bassador in Rome; Palazzo Venezia, Rome, from 1737; Manfrin Gallery, Venice (sold 1856, no. 10 in catalogue); American private collection, from 1857; American art market, 1917; Private collection, Paris; Samuel H. Kress Collection, 1956.

Literature: A. Marchesan, *Vita e prose scelte di Francesco Benaglio* (1894), (based upon a manuscript of 1743–57). Francesco Algarotti, *Opere*, XIII (1751), 217. Ernst Emmerling, *Pompeo Batoni* (Darmstadt, 1932), p. 131, no. 183. Anthony M. Clark, "Some Early Subject Pictures by P. G. Batoni," *The Burlington Magazine*, CI (June 1959), 232–236, fig. 32. North Carolina Museum of Art, *The Samuel H. Kress Collection* (Raleigh, 1960), pp. 122–123. Anthony M. Clark, "Batoni's Triumph of Venice," NCMA *Bulletin*, IV (Fall 1963), 4–11.

The subject which Foscarini commissioned from Batoni was to show "the flourishing state of the Venetian Republic when, in the peace following the Treaty of Cambrai, the fine arts were reborn, called forth and nurtured by Doge Leonardo Loredan (who ruled from 1501 to 1521) . . . with the sea, the prospect of the city, architecture, dignified personages and spirits of all sexes and ages, symbols of literature and the fine arts . . . ."

North Carolina Museum of Art
Samuel H. Kress Collection

7 Thomas, First Baron Dundas, 1741-1820

Oil on canvas, 117-1/2 x 77-1/2 inches. Signed and dated (beside nose of dog) : P. Batoni Pinxit Roma 1764.
Collection: Dundas Family.
Literature: John Steegman, "Some English Portraits by Pompeo Batoni," *The Burlington Magazine,* LXXXVIII (March 1946), 60, no. 37. Tony Ellis, "Pictures from Aske Hall Loaned by the Marquess of Zetland," *The Connoisseur,* CLII (January 1963), 36, fig. 4.

The Most Hon. The Marquess of Zetland
Aske Hall, Yorkshire, England

8 Hercules

Red chalk on prepared paper (orange), squared, 11 x 8-1/4 inches. Executed 1742.
Collections: British nineteenth-century private collection?; Mme. Veuve Galippe, Sale De Vries, Amsterdam, March 27-29, 1923, in lot 516; Dr. Fritz Haussman, Berlin, 1931; Countess Finckenstein, Switzerland, 1950's.
Literature: Ernst Emmerling, "Pompeo Batoni, Handzeichnung-Kleberand der Sammlung Haussmann Berlin," Manuscript catalogue, 1931, no. 11 (tracing), p. 15D. Ernst Emmerling, *Pompeo Batoni* (Darmstadt, 1932), p. 141, no. Z 12.
A study for the painting, *Choice of Hercules,* of 1742 now in the Uffizi (no. 8547). This drawing was in a large album of drawings by Batoni and Mengs (broken up in 1960, depleted earlier) presumably prepared in Rome in the second half of the eighteenth century and with early nineteenth-century British notations.

Anthony M. Clark, Minneapolis

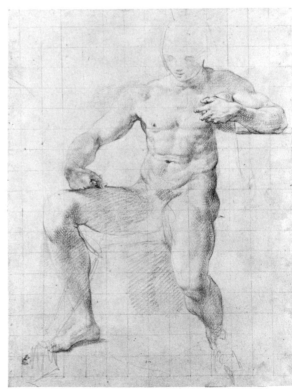

Pietro Bianchi

Rome 1694—Rome 1740

Though he achieved considerable fame during his lifetime. Bianchi has recently been almost totally neglected. His early work is stylistically dependent upon the Rococo, particularly the work of Luti. He later drew upon pre-Maratti Baroque painting to create a Neo-baroque style which approaches, but does not equal, the classicizing tendencies of Batoni.

9 *Argus and Mercury with Io*

Oil on canvas, 73-3/4 x 50-1/2 inches.
Collection: Given by the artist to Pietro Mancini (?).
Literature: Carlo Giuseppe Ratti, *Vite de pittori, scultori, ed architetti genovesi, di Raffaello Soprani* (Genoa, 1768–69). Anthony M. Clark, "Introduction to Pietro Bianchi," *Paragone,* XV (January 1964), 44-45, fig. 58.
Ratti describes a picture given by the artist to Pietro Mancini which is probably identical with the present canvas.

Paul H. Ganz, New York

Domenico Corvi

Viterbo 1721—Rome 1803

The work of Corvi's youth was Baroque in style. Under the influence of Mengs and Batoni, his manner became more classical in his mature and later works, but it was never rigorously so. He was the teacher of Cades and Camuccini.

10 *Head of a Boy*

Black and white chalk on faded blue paper, 7-3/8 x 6-3/8 inches. Inscribed (by Alessandro Maggiori): Il Corvi Fece. Executed ca.1780.
Collections: Alessandro Maggiori (purchased Rome, 1807); Argentieri; Breschi.

Anthony M. Clark, Minneapolis

11 *Glorification of Andrea Doria*

Oil on canvas, 38-3/4 x 19-3/8 inches. Painted ca.1775.
Collection: Doria d'Angri, Naples (as Tiepolo).
A *modello* for a ceiling decoration.

The Minneapolis Institute of Arts

Venice 1718/20—Venice 1785

Pietro Gaspari, together with his brother Giovanni Paolo, spent the most important part of his creative life designing theatre decors at the Bavarian court in Munich. In 1782 he returned to Venice where he was teacher of architecture and perspective at the Academy.

12 *A Roman Public Place*

Pen and black and bistre ink with ink washes on white paper, 10-1/2 x 16-1/2 inches.
Collection: L. B. (not recorded).
Exhibited: Minneapolis Institute of Art, "Theatre Drawings from the Donald Oenslager Collection," MIA *Bulletin*, LII (March 1963), 28, no. 38.

Donald Oenslager, New York

Giovanni Battista Piranesi

Mogliano near Mestre? 1720—Rome 1778

With the exception of a few years in Venice in the 1740's, Piranesi spent his artistic maturity working in Rome. He is most famous for his etchings which depict the remains of ancient Rome, and for the *Carceri*, a series of imaginary views of prisons. Piranesi was, by training, an architect. In the few buildings from his designs which were constructed, he demonstrated an early Neo-classic style. He exercised considerable influence upon young architects who came to Rome.

13 *The Temple of Isis at Pompeii*

Reed and quill pen and brown-black ink over preliminary indications in black chalk, on paper, 20-1/2 x 30-3/4 inches. Executed 1775–1778.
Collection: Marvin L. Levy, New York.
One of a series of drawings which Piranesi executed at the end of his life of monuments at Pompeii.

The Pierpont Morgan Library, New York

14 *View of the Forum of Nerva*

Etching, 18-3/4 x 27-15/16 inches.
Literature: Henri Focillon, *Giovanni-Battista Piranesi* (Paris, 1918), p. 52, no. 750 (33). Arthur M. Hind, *Giovanni Battista Piranesi* (London, 1922), no. 95, state II/IV. From the series of etchings, *Views of Rome.*

Leona E. Prasse, Cleveland

15 *View of the Temple of the Sibyl at Tivoli*

Etching, 16-3/4 x 25-1/8 inches.
Literature: Henri Focillon, *Giovanni-Battista Piranesi* (Paris, 1918), p. 53, no. 764 (47). Arthur M. Hind, *Giovanni Battista Piranesi* (London, 1922), no. 61, state III/V. From the series of etchings, *Views of Rome.*

Leona E. Prasse, Cleveland

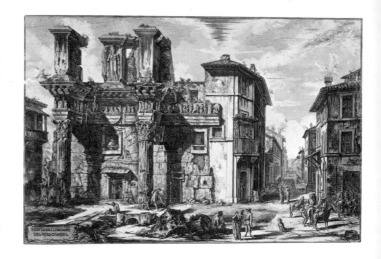

Carle Van Loo

Nice 1705—Paris 1765

Born into a family of painters of Flemish origin, the precocious Carle Van Loo was first a pupil of his brother Jean Baptiste. Van Loo's career was typical of that of a successful academic painter of the eighteenth century. He was active in Rome and Turin, as well as in Paris. In 1735 he became a member of the Academy, in 1749 director of the Ecole des élèves protégés, and in 1762 Premier Peintre du Roi.

Oil on canvas, 33 x 34 inches. Signed (lower right): Carle Vanloo. Painted ca.1754.
Collections: Mme. de Pompadour, Chateau of Bellevue; Baron Nathaniel de Rothschild, Vienna (no. 18 in the Catalogue of Collection).
Literature: "Four Recent Acquisitions," CPLH *Bulletin*, VIII (November-December 1950), 2-5.
Engraved in 1756 by St. Fessard. One of a set of four pictures representing the arts. Though in an academic late Baroque style, details of this picture, particularly the vase and the bust, display the beginnings of Neo-classicism.

California Palace of the Legion of Honor, San Francisco
Museum purchase, Mildred Anna Williams Collection

Jean Honoré Fragonard

Grasse 1732—Paris 1806

A pupil first of Chardin, then of Boucher, Fragonard won the *Prix de Rome* in 1752. He worked with Van Loo from 1753 till his departure for Rome in 1756. He remained there until 1761. Fragonard worked almost entirely for amateurs, receiving little official recognition. He varied his style considerably to suit particular commissions. Though in general his style may be described as Rococo, he did approach closely early Neo-classicism in a few works.

17 *Bacchanal*

Etching, 5-1/4 x 7-7/8 inches.
Literature: Prosper de Baudicour, *Le Peintre-Graveur Français continué*, I (Paris, 1859–61), 161, no. 6.
One of a set of four etchings.

The Cleveland Museum of Art
Dudley P. Allen and Charles W. Harkness Funds

Richard Wilson

*Penegoes, Montgomeryshire 1714—
Colommendy, Wales 1782*

The son of a Welsh clergyman, Wilson was given a good classical education. He came to London in the 1740's and set up as a portrait painter. He was in Italy in the 1750's, where he turned to landscape painting, drawing inspiration from Claude and Gaspar Poussin. After his return to England, Wilson continued to paint classical landscapes. His work was not well received during his lifetime.

Oil on canvas, 24-1/8 x 30-3/16 inches.
Collections: Broughton, Anglesey Abbey; Anonymous sale, Christie's, London, December 3, 1926, no. 98; T. T. Ellis, Worcester, Mass., 1927; Bequeathed by Mary G. Ellis to the Worcester Museum, 1940.
Literature: WAM *Annual*, IV (1941), 37, 38, 41, notes 5-6. William George Constable, *Richard Wilson* (Cambridge, Mass., 1953), p. 194. Constable entitles the composition, of which he calls the present picture an autograph version, *Lake Avernus I*.

Worcester Art Museum

**Richard Boyle
Third Earl of Burlington
and Fourth Earl of Cork**

19 *The Council Hall, Chichester, Sussex*

Pen and grey wash on paper, 12 x 17-3/4 inches. Inscribed (lower left) : A Draught of the Earl of Burlington's for the side front of a Councill house for the Corporation of Chichester. Executed ca.1730.
Collections: Lord Burlington; Dukes of Devonshire.
Literature: Fiske Kimball, "Burlington Architectus," RIBA *Journal*, XXXIV (October 15, 1927), 675, fig. 24.
This design, executed by Lord Burlington's draughtsman, Henry Flitcroft, was made about 1730, slightly earlier than that for the York Assembly Rooms, Burlington's most famous design.

Royal Institute of British Architects, London

1694—Chiswick 1753

Though to Colin Campbell must go credit for introducing Palladianism into England, it was Burlington's enthusiasm for the style which won for it early and widespread acceptance. Burlington's own designs demonstrate an almost pedantic purity in the use of classical sources, unique in Europe at that time. He worked closely with the architect and decorator William Kent (1685–1748) to create several of the most important examples of English Palladian architecture.

A Draught of the Earl of Burlington
for the side front of a Councill house
for the Corporation of Chichester

Johann Heinrich Tischbein the Elder

Haina 1722—Cassel 1789

Tischbein studied first in Germany. In 1748 he went to Paris where he worked under Carle Van Loo. The following year he was with Piazzetta in Venice. He was in Rome from 1750 to 1751. Tischbein returned to Germany in 1752, becoming in that year court painter to Wilhelm VIII of Hesse. He was also associated with the Cassel Academy.

20 *Anthony, Fatally Wounded, with Cleopatra*

Oil on canvas, 13-11/16 x 17-1/2 inches. Painted 1769.
Collection: Gallery of the Landgrafs of Hesse.
Literature: Joseph Friederich Engelschall, *Johann Heinrich Tischbein* (Nuremberg, 1797), p. 102, no. 39. Edmond Michel, *Les Tischbein* (Lyon, 1881), p. 14, no. 905. Oscar Eisenmann, *Katalog der Königl. Gemälde-Galerie zu Cassel* (Cassel, 1888), p. 377, no. 654. Hermann Bahlmann, *Johann Heinrich Tischbein* (Strassburg, 1911), pp. 27, 75, no. 59. *Katalog der Staatlichen Gemäldegalerie zu Kassel*, II (Berlin, 1929), 80, no. 689. Kurt Luthmer, *Die Hessische Malerfamilie Tischbein* (Cassel, 1934), p. 18, nos. 41 and 42. Eberhard Preime, *Die Handzeichnungen von Johann Heinrich Tischbein* (Cassel, n.d.), p. 89. Hans Vogel, *Katalog der Staatlichen Gemäldegalerie zu Kassel* (Cassel, 1958), p. 71, no. 689.

From the same series as the picture which follows, *Augustus with the Dying Cleopatra*. Two other compositions from that series are in the Busch-Reisinger Museum, Harvard University A composition identical to the present picture, but with life-size figures, is in a private collection at Winterbüren near Cassel, dated 1767. A series of paintings depicting the story of Cleopatra in large scale once belonged to the Weissenstein wing of the Castle of Wilhelmshöhe. Fragments of that series are preserved by the administration of the Staatliche Schloesser in Hesse. A brush and ink drawing of the composition, dated 1768, was on the Munich art market in 1931. A replica of the composition, signed and dated 1774, is in the Landesmuseum, Oldenburg.

Staatliche Kunstsammlungen Kassel

21 *Augustus with the Dying Cleopatra*

Oil on canvas, 13-11/16 x 17-1/2 inches. Signed and dated (lower right): J. H. Tischbein Pinx. 1769.
Collection: See preceding entry.
Literature: See preceding entry. Engelschall, p. 103, no. 43. Michel, no. 904. Eisenmann, no. 653. Bahlmann, pp. 28, 75, no. 58. *Katalog* (1929), no. 688. Luthmer, p. 19, no. 47. Vogel, no. 688.
From the same series as the picture which precedes.

Staatliche Kunstsammlungen Kassel

22 *Eros Taught by Orpheus*

Pen and ink on white paper, 10 x 9-1/2 inches. Signed
(lower right) : 99/Tischbein. . . .
Collection: Edwin B. Crocker, purchased in Dresden in
1871.
Exhibited: Detroit Institute of Arts, German Paintings
and Drawings from the Time of Goethe in American Collections, no. 138. Catalogue published *Art Quarterly*, XII
(Summer 1949), 231-256.

Crocker Art Gallery, Sacramento

Gavin Hamilton

Lanarkshire 1723—Rome 1789

Hamilton first went to Rome in the 1740's to study
painting. He was again in England in the early 1750's
where he produced a few portraits before returning
permanently to Rome. By 1760 Hamilton was painting Poussinesque historical pictures which are possibly the first truly Neo-classic paintings to have
been created. In Rome he functioned as a dealer in
antiquities, as well as a painter. Engravings after
his paintings were widely influential throughout
Europe, and he also furthered Neo-classicism by
means of personal contact with young artists in Rome.

23 *Innocence*

Engraving by Domenico Cunego after a painting by Gavin
Hamilton, 18-1/8 x 10-7/8 inches. Inscribed: Gavinus
Hamilton pinxit 1766/Dominicus Cunego sculpt. Romae.
Literature: Charles Le Blanc, *Manuel de L'Amateur
D'Estampes*, II (Paris, 1856–1888), 76, no. 54.
The house with a conical roof in the distance may reflect
Laugier's theories of the beginnings of architecture.

The Cleveland Museum of Art
Gift of Mrs. Frederick C. Merrick

Charles Louis Clérisseau

Paris 1721—Auteuil 1820

Clérisseau studied first in Paris under Blondel. In 1746 he won the *Prix de Rome*, but did not leave for Italy until 1749. In 1753 he ran into difficulties with the director of the French Academy, Natoire. He left for home in 1754, but got no farther than Florence, where he met Robert Adam in January 1755. For several years Clérisseau served Adam as teacher and draughtsman. In 1766 he finally left Italy, returning to Paris. He passed the year 1771 in London, where he won acclaim at the Royal Academy exhibit. Projects of his later life included publication of *Les Antiquités de la France* and work for Katherine II of Russia.

24 *View of the Roman Forum with the Basilica of Maxentius (Constantine)*

Pen, ink and wash, 7 x 15 inches. Remains of a signature, lower left. Executed ca.1756.
Collection: Dr. C. R. Rudolf, London.
A related drawing, given to Robert Adam and perhaps done after the present drawing or at the same moment, is published in John Fleming, *Robert Adam and his Circle in Edinburgh and Rome* (London, 1962), pl. 52.

Mr. and Mrs. Thomas J. McCormick, Poughkeepsie

25 *Temple of Minerva at Assisi*

Pen with sepia and water color, 16 x 20 inches. Executed
ca.1762–1767.

Wells College, Aurora, New York

26 *Classical Landscape*

Body color on paper, 14-1/8 x 11-13/16 inches. Executed
ca.1760–1770.

Mr. and Mrs. Thomas J. McCormick, Poughkeepsie

Anton Raffael Mengs

Assig, Bohemia 1728—Rome 1779

Mengs was the son of the Dresden court painter, Ismaël Mengs. He studied first with his father, and was taken to Rome in 1741. He was back in Dresden in 1746, and was made First Painter to the King, but he elected to return to Rome where, in 1755, he came under the influence of Winckelmann. Shortly thereafter, his mature style and his popularity were achieved. He worked principally in Rome and Madrid for the remainder of his life.

27 *The Entombment (Lamentation?)*

Charcoal heightened with white, on grey-green paper, 61-1/4 x 46-5/8 inches. Inscribed (on mat): HUIC TABULAE EXTREMOS DUM DUCIT ARUNDINE TRACTUS MENGSIUS INFELIX PROH DOLOR.
Collections: Mrs. George H. Chickering, Boston, 1887; given by Mrs. George L. Nichols, 1922.
Exhibited: Museum of Art, Rhode Island School of Design, The Age of Canova, 1957, no. 100, repro. p. 23.
A similar drawing is mentioned in Jose Nicolas de Azara, *The Works of Anthony Rafael Mengs*, I (London, 1796), 31-32 and reproduced Prado, Madrid, Antonio Rafael Mengs, 1929.

The Museum of Fine Arts, Boston

Laurent Pécheux

Lyon 1729—Turin 1821

Though born in France, Pécheux spent the greater part of his life in Italy. He was in Rome from 1752 to 1796, where he was a pupil of Mengs and Batoni, and was influenced by Hamilton. In 1796 he went to Turin, where he was court painter and director of the Academy.

28 *Apollo Pierced by the Arrows of Two Amorini*

Attributed to Laurent Pécheux

Oil on canvas, 23-1/2 x 19-3/4 inches.

Collection: Acquired in 1902 with the purchase of the Massarenti Collection, Rome.

Literature: E. van Esbroeck, *Catalogue du Musée de peinture, sculpture et archéologie au Palais Accoramboni* [*i.e.*, the Massarenti Collection], I (Rome, 1897), 148, no. 859 (as Nicholas Poussin).

The attribution to Pécheux was suggested by Anthony M. Clark.

The Walters Art Gallery, Baltimore

Cristoforo Unterberger

Cavalese 1732—Rome 1798

Born into a family of artists, Unterberger studied first in Vienna where he became an Academician in 1753. In 1758 he arrived in Rome where he spent the rest of his life. He soon came under the influence of Mengs. In 1772 he became a member of the Accademia di San Luca. After Mengs' death in 1779, Unterberger received important commissions and became one of the chief painters of Italy.

29 Two Designs for Decorations

A. *Sculpture*. Oil on canvas, 43-1/4 x 12 inches. Labeled on stretcher: Lady Leslie & Seymour Leslie/Carracci panels —4/4 submitted to Vatican for Torso Room Decorations— 2 Flesh 2 grey.
B. *Painting*. Oil on canvas, 43-3/16 x 12 inches. Labeled on stretcher: Lady Leslie & Seymour Leslie/Carracci panels 4/3.
Painted ca.1780.
Collections: Sir John and Lady Leslie; Seymour Leslie, Sale, Sotheby & Co., London, July 29, 1942, p. 11, no. 61; Sale, Sotheby & Co., London, April 25, 1956, no. 169 (property of a gentleman).
Literature: Anthony M. Clark, "Four Decorative Panels by Unterberger," WAM *Annual*, IX (1961), 1-11.
Painting and *Sculpture* were models for fresco decorations extant in the Sala del Torso, Museo Vaticano. The influence of Raphael's decorations in the Vatican Loggia can be discerned in the design of these decorations. The *ignudi* who appear to support elements of ornament reflect the style of the Carraccis.

Worcester Art Museum

Carlo Marchionni

Rome 1702—Rome 1786

Marchionni functioned as an architect, engineer, sculptor, and caricaturist. He was a pupil of Bargioni. In 1728 he won a first prize at the Accademia di San Luca. He became a fellow of the Accademia in 1740 and Princeps in 1775. Marchionni was active largely in Rome, executing several papal commissions.

30 Design for the Door Case to the Grand Gallery of the Villa Albani, Rome

Pencil, pen and ink with grey wash, on paper, 16 x 7-11/16 inches. Executed ca.1756.
Collections: Piancastelli, Rome, 1904; Brandegee, Brookline, Mass., 1904–1938.
Literature: Rudolf Berliner, "Zeichnungen von Carlo und Filippo Marchionni," *Münchner Jahrbuch der bildenden Kunst*, III, nos. 9-10 (1958–59), 306, fig. 57. Richard P. Wunder, *Extravagant Drawings of the Eighteenth Century* (New York, 1962), no. 22.
The architect Marchionni was commissioned about 1756 to design the interior decoration of Cardinal Albani's villa just outside the walls of Rome. The family arms appear in the central shell motif of the present drawing.

The Cooper Union Museum, New York

Joseph Marie Vien

Montpellier 1716—Paris 1809

Vien was first a student of Natoire at the Academy in Paris. He won the *Prix de Rome* in 1743. For the next seven years he studied in Rome and was there considered a realist. Vien was made a member of the Academy in 1754. He enjoyed enormous fame during his lifetime. The most notable of his many pupils was Jacques Louis David. His work became progressively more Neo-classic in style as he grew older. At his death he was a senator, a Count of the Empire, and a Commander of the Legion of Honor.

31 *Love Prepared for His Triumph*

Pen and sepia wash, on paper, 8 x 11-1/4 inches. Signed and dated (left center): Vien 1796.
Literature: Ernest Scheyer, "French Drawings of the Great Revolution and the Napoleonic Era," *Art Quarterly*, IV (1941), 188, 191, fig. 1.

The Detroit Institute of Arts

32 *Greek Lady at the Bath*

Oil on canvas, 35-1/2 x 26-1/2 inches. Signed and dated
(at left) : J. M. Vien 1767.
Collections: Duc de Choiseul; Servatius; Rhone; Sir
George Roberts; Mme. Elisa Doucet.
Literature: Charles Blanc, *Le Trésor de la Curiosité*, I
(Paris, 1857–58), 199. Sale, Sotheby & Co., London, June
19, 1957, p. 25, no. 188. F. J. B. Watson, *The Choiseul Box*
(New York, 1963), p. 13, fig. 4.
Engraved in 1772 by Nicolas Ponce for the *Galerie de
Choiseul.*

Ponce Museum of Art, Puerto Rico
Luis A. Ferré Foundation

Jean-Baptiste Greuze

Tournus 1725–Paris 1805

Greuze's first experience as a painter was in the picture factory of Grandon at Lyon. He won early success in the Salon of 1755 with a sentimental genre picture. It was this sort of picture which earned Diderot's praise and popular success for Greuze. In 1769 he submitted *Septimus Severus Reproaching Caracalla* as his reception piece to the Academy. It was poorly received. Thereafter Greuze relied upon private exhibitions and sales of his work. Patronage of his work declined, especially after the Revolution.

33 *Septimus Severus Reproaching Caracalla*

Oil on canvas, 48-13/16 x 63 inches. Painted in 1769.
Collection: Ancient Collection of the Academy.
Exhibition: Paris, Salon, 1769.
Literature: L'espion anglais ou correspondance entre Milord All'Eye et Milord 'Ear, X (London, 1784), Letter XI, January 4, 1779. Edmond and Jules de Goncourt, *L'Art au XVIIIème Siècle* (Paris, 1873), pp. 382-399. Denis Diderot, *Oeuvres complètes,* X (Paris, 1876), 438. Charles Normand, *J. B. Greuze* (Paris, n.d.), p. 86 ff. Camille Mauclair, *Jean-Baptiste Greuze* (Paris, 1907), cat. p. 4, no. 16. André Fontaine, *Les Collections de l'Académie Royale de Peinture et de Sculpture* (Paris, 1910), p. 200, no. 552-132. Louis Hautecoeur, *Greuze* (Paris, 1913), p. 58, pl. XI. Gaston Brière, *Catalogue des peintures françaises du Musée du Louvre* (Paris, 1924), no. 368. Anita Brookner, "Jean-Baptiste Greuze—I," *The Burlington Magazine,* XCVIII (May 1956), 161-162, fig. 41. Henry Bardon, "Les Peintures à sujets antiques au XVIIIe siècle d'après les livrets de Salons," *Gazette des Beaux-Arts,* VI period, LXI (April 1963), 219, 224, fig. 1.
Bardon identifies the source of the subject of the present picture as from de Rollin, *l'Histoire romaine,* pp. 642-643.

Musée du Louvre, Paris

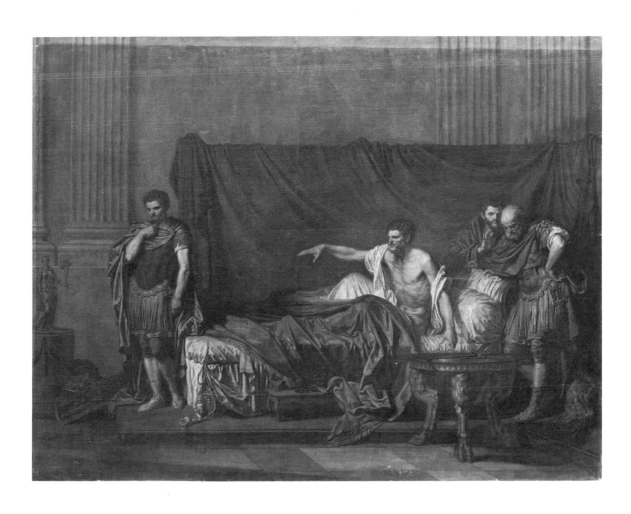

Louis-Jean-François Lagrenée
the Elder

Paris 1724—Paris 1805

Lagrenée was the pupil of Carle Van Loo. He won the *Prix de Rome* in 1749, was made a member of the Academy in 1755, and became Premier Peintre to Elizabeth of Russia in 1760. He was made director of the French Academy in Rome in 1781. Lagrenée was a prolific painter. Between 1755 and 1785 he exhibited more than 150 pictures.

34 *Mercury Entrusting the Infant Bacchus to the Nymphs of the Isle of Naxos*

Oil on canvas, 39-3/8 x 32-1/4 inches. Painted ca.1773.
Collections: Comte d'Antray, Paris, 18th c.; deposited by the State, an VII (1799).
Exhibited: Paris, Salon, 1773.
Literature: H. Jouin, *Musée d'Angers, Peintures, Sculptures* (Angers, 1881), p. 27, no. 92. *Inventaire général des richesses d'Art de la France, Province monuments civils,* III (Paris, 1885), 28-29. Louis Gonse, *Les Chef d'Oeuvre des Musées de France—Peinture* (Paris, 1900), p. 43. Marcel Valotaire, *Le Musée d'Angers* (Paris, 1928), p. 14 fig. 44. M. Sandoz, "L. J. F. Lagrenée dit l'Ainé," *Bulletin Société Historique de l'Art Français* (1961), pp. 130-131.

Musée des Beaux Arts, Angers

Jean Bernard Restout

Paris 1732—Paris 1797

Son of the well-known painter Jean Restout, Jean Bernard won the second *Prix de Rome* in 1755, and went to Italy. He was received into the Academy in 1769 and made professor in 1771. In 1793 he was president of the Commune des Arts and commissaire of the Garde-Meuble.

35 *Philemon and Baucis Give Hospitality to Jupiter and Mercury*

Oil on canvas, 46-7/8 x 64-1/8 inches. Painted in 1769.
Collections: Ancient Collection of the Academy; Louvre, Galerie d'Apollon, Inventory an II (1796); Sent from the Central Museum, an XI (1803).
Exhibited: Paris, Salon, 1771, no. 139; Mondaye (Abbaye des Prémontrés near Bayeux), Les Restout, 1956 (catalogue summarized in *Art de Basse-Normandie*, no. 2 (Summer 1956), 37-38.
Literature: André Fontaine, *Les Collections de l'Académie Royale de Peinture et de Sculpture* (Paris, 1910), p. 197. Jean Locquin, *La Peinture d'Histoire en France* (Paris, 1912), p. 233. J. E. Weelen, *Bulletin de la Société Dunoise* (Châteaudun, 1956–57), p. 13.
Served as Restout's *morceau de réception* to the Academy. It was accepted November 25, 1769.

Musée des Beaux-Arts de Tours

Hubert Robert

Paris 1733—Paris 1808

Robert studied with Michel-Ange Slodtz, who suggested that he go to Italy. He did so in 1754. There Robert became a friend of Piranesi and Panini, won favor with the French ambassador, the future Duc de Choiseul, and traveled to Southern Italy and Sicily with Fragonard and the Abbé de Saint-Non. Robert returned to France in 1765, and in a short time became a member of the Academy and established himself as a painter and decorator. He became keeper of Louis XVI's pictures and was later one of the first curators of the Louvre.

36 *The Finding of the Laocoön*

Oil on canvas, 47 x 64 inches. Signed and dated (base of statue at far right): H. Robert 1773.

The imaginary Roman basilica which Robert here created recalls the Grand Gallery of the Louvre. The Hellenistic sculptural group, *The Laocoön*, was found in Rome in 1506.

The Virginia Museum of Fine Arts, Glasgow Fund

Jean Michel Moreau
called Moreau le jeune

Paris 1741—Paris 1814

Moreau le jeune was a pupil in the studio of Louis Joseph Le Lorrain. He went with his master to St. Petersburg in 1758, where he was employed in making designs for theatrical decors. After Le Lorrain's death in 1760, Moreau returned to Paris. He soon made a reputation for himself as a designer of book illustrations. In 1770 he was made draughtsman to the Menus Plaisirs du Roi. Moreau made a journey to Italy in 1785 and returned with a style which was closer to that of Vien and David than his earlier work had been. He was made a member of the Academy in 1789 and held some official positions after the Revolution.

37 *Hekate, Artemis and the Erinnyes* (?)

Pen and wash heightened with white, 13-3/4 x 17-1/2 inches.

The subject is uncertain; it resembles in general character the drawings which Moreau made to be engraved, but, perhaps because of the uncertainty of subject represented, it has not been identified with any item in the catalogue of engravings after Moreau.

Museum of Art, Rhode Island School of Design

Paris 1730—Paris 1809

A pupil of J.-B. Lemoyne II, Pajou won first prize at the Ecole royale des élèves protégés in 1748. He worked at the French Academy in Rome from 1752 to 1756. Pajou became a member of the Academy in 1760, professor in 1766, and rector in 1792. Beginning in 1777, he was curator of antiquities.

38 *Project for the Tomb of the Maréchal Charles-Louis-Auguste Fouquet, Duc de Belle-Isle*

Pencil, pen and ink with water colors, on brown paper, 35-1/2 x 22-1/4 inches. Signed and dated (lower right): Pajou inve. fe. 1761.

Collections: Vicomte Gaspard de Bizemont, Paris, 1837; Alfred Hubert, Paris, 1876; E.H.R. (not identified); John J. Peoli, New York, 1894; Sarah Cooper Hewitt, New York.

Literature: Michel N. Benisovich, "Drawings of the Sculptor Augustin Pajou in the United States," *Art Bulletin*, XXXV (December 1953), 295-298, fig. 10. Benisovich, "Some Drawings by European Masters in United States Museum Collections," *Art Quarterly*, XXXII (Spring 1959), 59-60, fig. 4. Richard P. Wunder, *Extravagant Drawings of the Eighteenth Century* (New York, 1962), no. 10.

The allegory of the drawing is explained by the following inscription: "The Maréchal enters the sepulchral chamber containing the tombs of his wife and son, the Count of Gisors, who both predeceased him. Their spirits are supposed to have left their tombs in order to greet him, and the Angel of Death is shutting the door of the sepulchral chamber in order to indicate that the Maréchal was the last of his family." Because the family was bankrupt, this project was not executed.

The Cooper Union Museum, New York

Antoine François Callet

Paris 1741—Paris 1823

A pupil of Boizot, Callet won the first prize for painting in 1759, the *Prix de Rome* in 1764, and was received into the Academy in 1780 on the strength of his picture *Cybele Crowned by Flora and Zephyr*, painted for the ceiling of the Galerie d'Apollon of the Louvre. During the Napoleonic era, Callet painted a number of battle scenes. He was also a distinguished portraitist.

39 *Achilles and the Body of Patroclus*

Bister wash over black and red chalk with opaque white, 14-1/2 x 17-3/4 inches.
Collection: Nemes Collection, Munich; Albert de Burlet, Berlin.
Literature: Georg Swarzenski, *Franzoesische Mappe des Achtzehnten, Mappen des Marées Gesellschaft* (Munich), pl. 27 (as Claude Michel Clodion, Classical Composition). Ernst Scheyer, "French Drawings of the Great Revolution and the Napoleonic Era," *Art Quarterly,* IV (Summer 1941), 193-194, fig. 6.
Perhaps related to a picture by Callet of the same subject in the Museum of St. Omer, France.

The Detroit Institute of Arts

40 *A Sacrifice in the Temple of Jupiter*

Attributed to Antoine François Callet

Pen, brown ink, and grey wash, on blue paper, 14-7/16 x
22-15/16 inches.

Literature: H[ugh] J. G[ourley], "Recent Additions to the
Collection of the Museum of Art," RISD *Museum Notes,*
L (May 1964), 6.

Museum of Art, Rhode Island School of Design

Versailles 1741—Paris 1828

Houdon was the most famous French sculptor of the
eighteenth century. He was a pupil of Lemoyne and
Pigalle. He won the first prize of the Academy in
1761. From 1764 to 1769 he worked in Rome, producing the well-known *St. Bruno* in Santa Maria degli
Angeli. He was made a member of the Academy in
1777. He retired in 1814, but continued to teach at
the Ecole des Beaux-Arts until 1823. Houdon was
quite successful in his lifetime. He had a large studio
and many pupils.

41 *Sorrow Consoled by Justice,*
Who Exhibits Fame
Allegory on the Death of M. Guillard

Pencil and charcoal heightened with white, on tan paper
13-1/2 x 17 inches. Signed and dated (lower right): hou-
don inve. 1774 [?].
Collections: Jacques Victor; Comte de la Beraudière,
Paris (Sale, 1883, no. 141); Marius Paulme, Paris (Sale,
Galerie Georges Petit, Paris, May 13, 1929, no. 107);
Mrs. Gustav Radeke, Providence.
Exhibited: Versailles, Bibliothèque, Exposition du Cen-
tenaire de Houdon, 1928, no. 78. Paris, Galerie Buvelot,
Exposition du Centenaire de Houdon, 1928, no. 105.
Literature: Hippolyte Mireur, *Dictionnaire des Ventes
d'Art faites en France et à l'Etranger . . . ,* III (Paris,
1911), 494. Paul Vitry, "Houdon Dessinateur," *Beaux-
Arts,* no. 7 (May 1, 1928), 100-101. Vitry, "Le Centenaire

de Houdon," *Revue de l'art Ancien et Moderne,* LIV
(June-December 1928), 18-20, 58-59, 68. M. A. Banks,
"The Radeke Collection of Drawings," RISD *Bulletin,*
XIX (October 1931), p. 66.
M. Guillard was counsellor of the Great Chamber of the
Parliament of Paris. He died in 1772.

Museum of Art, Rhode Island School of Design

Chalon-sur-Saône 1735—Paris 1814

Boichot was a pupil of the ornamental-sculptor Colasson in Chalon and of Challe in Paris. He also studied in Rome. His early work was done in the provinces, but in 1788 he became an associate of the Academy. After the Revolution he received several important commissions for architectural decorations and portraits.

42 *Hercules Personifying Force*

Bronze, 35 inches high. Executed ca.1795.
Collection: William Randolph Hearst.
Literature: Francis H. Dowley, "A Neo-Classic Hercules," *Art Quarterly,* XV (Spring 1952), 73-76.
The present sculpture was a model for the sculpture of heroic scale which Boichot executed to decorate the portico of Ste.-Geneviève in Paris just after it had been converted into the Pantheon.

Los Angeles County Museum of Art
The William Randolph Hearst Collection

Claude Michel, called Clodion

Nancy 1738—Paris 1814

At the age of seventeen Clodion came to Paris where
he studied with his uncle, Lambert Sigisbert Adam,
and later with Pigalle. In 1762 he went to Rome. He
worked at the French Academy there until 1767 and
remained in Rome until 1771. Clodion worked almost
entirely for private patrons, receiving few public or
royal commissions. The frank sensuality of his style
caused him to fall from favor at the time of the
Revolution. He retired to Nancy for a few years, but
an alteration of his style obtained for him some public
commissions at the end of his life.

43 *Young Girl*

Terra cotta, 17-3/4 inches high. Signed (lower rear):
CLODION.
Collections: May be identical with "Vestale debout tenant
un plateau sur lequel se trouve une couronne de fleurs.
Statuette en terre cuite. Haut. O^m 44," which was in-
cluded in the sale of Eugène Tondu, April, 1866. See
Stanislas Lami, *Dictionnaire des Sculpteurs . . . au Dix-
Huitième Siècle*, II (Paris, 1911), 154; Mrs. Grace Rainey
Rogers.
Literature: William M. Milliken, "The Rousseau de la
Rottière Room," CMA *Bulletin*, XXIX (April 1942), 62,
66.

The Cleveland Museum of Art
Gift of Grace Rainey Rogers
in memory of her father, William J. Rainey

44 *Satyress and Child*

Terra cotta, diameter 12-1/8 inches. Signed (recto, lower right): CLODION. Inscribed (verso): A/L'ami Jean./Souvenir offert/en Mai/1803.

Clodion had previously employed a composition similar to that of the present relief in a large scale relief made to decorate the exterior of the Hôtel de Bourbon-Condé in Paris, now in the Metropolitan Museum of Art.

The Cleveland Museum of Art
Gift of Mr. and Mrs. Ralph King

45 *Pair of Candelabra*

Patinated bronze with gilt bronze candle branches and grey marble and gilt bronze bases, 36-1/2 inches high. Signed (behind rocks): CLODION.

Collections: The Marquis of Hertford; Sir Richard Wallace; Mrs. Grace Rainey Rogers.

Literature: William M. Milliken, "The Rousseau de la Rottière Room," CMA *Bulletin*, XXIX (April 1942), 53, 66.

The Cleveland Museum of Art
Gift of Grace Rainey Rogers
in memory of her father, William J. Rainey

Died Paris 1783

Perlin was trained as an architect, but he is noted primarily for his water-color renderings of architecture. He did, however, design the court facade of the Hotel Montmorency.

46 *Homage to a Hero*

Pencil, pen and ink, with water color, on paper, 13-3/4 x 20 inches. Signed and dated (lower left): F. Perlin 1772. *Collections:* Paignon-Dijonval, Paris (Sale, Paris, 1810, no. 4005); Double, Paris; Léon Decloux, Sèvres, until 1911.

A classical hero receives homage from personifications of arts and sciences. Two putti carry a medallion with the monogram "V S."

The Cooper Union Museum, New York

Niklas Lafrensen
called Lavreince

Stockholm 1737—Stockholm 1807

Lafrensen was a miniaturist and painter in water colors. He studied first with his father, who bore the same name. After his father's death in 1756, Lafrensen came to Paris, where he resided for three years. Upon his return to Sweden, he obtained success as a history painter, water colorist, and portrait painter. He returned to Paris in 1771 and remained there, except for a short visit to Stockholm, until 1791. He won great popularity with his water colors which were frequently reproduced in engravings.

Etched state before the first state of the engraving by François Dequevauviller, 13 x 18-1/4 inches (size of subject). Executed ca.1783.
Literature: Roger Portalis and Henri Béraldi, *Les Graveurs du 18e Siècle*, I, part II (Paris, 1880), 744, no. 1. H. W. Lawrence and B. L. Dighton, *French Line Engravings of the Late XVIII Century* (London, 1910), p. 20, pl. VI, no. 44.
Cincinnati Art Museum, Bequest of Herbert Greer French

Victor Louis

Paris 1731—Paris 1800

Louis was one of the many talented men who en-
riched the French architectural heritage in the last
half of the eighteenth century. He entered the school
of the Academy of Architecture in 1746 and studied
under Loriot. He was in Rome from 1756 to 1759. In
1764 Louis was made architect to the King of Poland,
and went there in 1765. Though he soon returned to
France, he remained titular architect to the king.
Louis' most famous building is the Theatre in Bordeaux.

48 Design for the Ballroom
of the Royal Palace at Warsaw
as Decorated for a Festival

Pen and ink with water color, on paper, 10-15/16 x 18-1/4
inches. Executed ca.1765.
Collection: Léon Decloux, Sèvres.
The Cooper Union Museum, New York

Louis Gustave Taraval

Stockholm 1738—Paris 1794

Taraval belonged to a family of many artists. He functioned as an architect and engraver. In 1754 Taraval went to Paris and became Inspecteur des Bâtiments du Roi. The most important part of his *oeuvre* is his designs for interior architecture.

49 Elevation of the Chimney Wall of a Salon

Pencil, pen and ink with water color, on paper, 16-15/16 x 26-5/8 inches. Signed (lower left) : LGT; (lower right) : Composé et dessiné par Gustave Taraval architecte Inspecteur des Batimens du Roy. Executed ca.1785.
Collections: Hippolyte Destailleur, Paris (Sale, Paris, May 19, 1896, no. 530) ; Léon Decloux, Sèvres.
Exhibited: The Detroit Institute of Arts, French Taste of the Eighteenth Century, 1956, no. 207.

The Cooper Union Museum, New York

Jean Charles Delafosse

Paris 1734—Paris 1789

The published designs of Delafosse have associated his name with the early phase of Neo-classic style in ornamental designs. His major published works were the *Nouvelle Iconologie Historique* of 1768, the *Decorations, Sculptures, Orfèvreries et Ornaments divers*, and the *Ameublement*.

50 Design for a Decorative Ewer

Pencil, pen and black ink with ink wash, on paper, 9-1/2 x 6-1/8 inches. Signed (lower left): J. C. Delafosse. Executed ca.1765.

Collection: Léon Decloux, Sèvres, until 1911.
Exhibited: Cooper Union Museum—American Federation of Arts travelling exhibition, Five Centuries of Drawing, 1959–1961, no. 59. A slight modification of this design was published in Delafosse, *Nouvelle Iconologie Historique . . .* (Paris, 1771), pl. 64 (series C, pl. 6), with the title *Abondance.*

The Cooper Union Museum, New York

51 Design for a Decorative Ewer

Pencil, pen, and black ink with ink wash, on paper, 9-7/16 x 6 inches. Signed (lower left): J. C. delafosse. Executed ca.1765.
Collection: Léon Decloux, Sèvres, until 1911.
Literature: Richard P. Wunder, *Extravagant Drawings of the Eighteenth Century* (New York, 1962), no. 66.

The Cooper Union Museum, New York

Jean-François Dapcher

ca.1721—Paris 1780

In 1743 at the age of 22, Dapcher apprenticed himself to Thomas Germain, goldsmith to the king and one of the most famous of all French silversmiths. In 1751 he was received as master. By 1776 he was no longer included in the list of Paris silversmiths. Dapcher's work is rather rare today.

52 Tureen with Cover, Stand, and Liner

Silver, 13-1/2 inches high, 19-1/4 inches in diameter (overall measurements). Tureen and stand marked with maker's mark, charge and discharge marks; cover and stand marked with date letter, crowned "K," and other marks. Executed 1773–1774.

Collections: Count Alexander Sergeevitch Stroganov (1733–1811); Dr. Ricardo de Espirito Santo Silva, Lisbon.

Exhibited: Paris, Musée des Arts Decoratifs, Les Trésors de l'orfèvrerie du Portugal, 1954, no. 365.

The Art Institute of Chicago

René Dubois

Paris 1737—Paris 1799

René was the son of a notable cabinetmaker, Jacques Dubois (ca.1693–1763). He was made a master in 1754, but continued to work with his father until the latter's death. Afterwards, his mother operated the shop, branding its products with her deceased husband's stamp. René's brother, Louis Dubois (1732–ca.1790), was a sculptor as well as a cabinetmaker. He is thought to have been responsible for the carved wood and cast bronze ornament used on furniture made in the shop. René Dubois was especially popular with Marie-Antoinette. He was made Ebéniste de la Reine in 1779.

53 Commode

Ebony veneer with Japanese lacquer panels, gilt bronze mounts, and marble top, 34-3/16 inches high, 60 inches wide (without marble top). Stamped twice (top front corners): I. Dubois JME. Executed ca.1765.
Collections: Frederick VI of Denmark(?); Earl of Plymouth; Mrs. Elisabeth Severance Prentiss.
Literature: Catalogue of the Elisabeth Severance Prentiss Collection (Cleveland, 1944), pp. 41-42, no. 18, pl. XIII. Charles Packer, *Paris Furniture* (Newport, England, 1956), p. 48, fig. 95. [Jean Meuvret], *Les Ebénistes du XVIIIᵉ siècle Français* (Paris, 1963), p. 222, fig. 3.
A very similar commode, stamped Dubois, is in the collection at Waddesdon Manor, England. The Cleveland Museum possesses a pair of corner cabinets, also by Dubois, which are quite similar in design to the present commode. The close relationship of the style of this commode to the designs of Delafosse has been noted by several authors.

The Cleveland Museum of Art
The Elisabeth Severance Prentiss Collection

Jean-Baptiste II Tilliard
(Jacques-Jean-Baptiste Tilliard)

Died Paris 1797

Tilliard was the son of a well-known chairmaker. He received the necessary papers to become master in 1752, but he did not actually register until 1764, when his father retired and he took over the family workshop. He had probably played an important role in the operation of the shop even before that date. As his father had before him, Tilliard worked for the Crown. He cooperated closely with the carver Chaillon and the gilder Mathon. At the time of the Revolution he chose to close his shop and retire.

54 Pair of Chairs

Carved and gilded wood, with modern upholstery, 40-1/8 inches high. Each chair stamped (on rear crosspiece): Tilliard. Executed ca.1765.
Literature: [Jean Meuvret], *Les Ebénistes du XVIIIe siècle Français* (Paris, 1963), pp. 252-253.

The Cleveland Museum of Art
Purchase from the J. H. Wade Fund

55 Model for the Lower Part
of a Carved-wood Panel

Anonymous, France

Red wax on wood panel, 13 x 15-1/2 inches. Executed ca.1780–1790.
Collection: Beurdeley (?).
The making of a wax model for a carved wooden panel indicates the care which was sometimes lavished upon decorative works in France in the eighteenth century.

Lent anonymously

François Marie Isidore Quéverdo

Josselin 1748–Paris 1797

Quéverdo was active in Paris as an engraver, designer of vignettes, and painter. He was a pupil of Pierre and de Longueil.

56 Designs for Arabesque Panels
with Attributes of *Autumn* and *Fishing*

Pen and ink with ink wash, on paper, 6-3/8 x 1-7/16 inches (each drawing). Inscribed (on mat): F. M. Queverdo/ 1788.
Collections: Blind stamp of a quatrefoil (unidentified); Léon Decloux, Sèvres, until 1911.

The Cooper Union Museum, New York

Active Paris 1780–1796

Lalonde was a prolific decorative designer and produced a number of engravings for furniture during the last years of the 1780's. His major published work is *Oeuvres diverses. . . .* Lalonde was, on occasion, employed by the Garde-Meuble to design furniture for the royal palaces.

Rouen 1738—Paris 1826

Lebarbier was a painter, a designer of engravings, and a theoretician of art. He was a pupil of Pierre at the Academy. After a trip to Rome and Switzerland, he was made an associate of the Academy in 1780 and a member in 1785. He exhibited frequently at the Salons and made book illustrations.

57 Design for a Console Table

Pencil, pen and black ink, with ink wash, on paper, 12-1/4 x 7-11/16 inches. Executed ca.1785–1790.
Collections: Eugène Rodrigues, Paris; Léon Decloux, Sèvres, after 1906 and until 1911.
Exhibited: Montreal Museum of Fine Arts, The Eighteenth Century, 1950, no. 82.
There exist drawings by Lalonde which he prepared in 1788 for consoles intended for the Salon des Jeux at Saint-Cloud.

The Cooper Union Museum, New York

58 Design of a Candlestick

Pencil, pen and ink, with water color, on paper, 13-1/2 x 7-11/16 inches. Executed ca.1790.
Collections: François Renaud, Paris; Léon Decloux, Sèvres, until 1911.
Peace stands beside an upright gun barrel.

The Cooper Union Museum, New York

Adam Weisweiler

Neuwied? ca.1750—after 1809

As was the case with many cabinetmakers working in France in the eighteenth century, Weisweiler was born in Germany. He studied there with David Roentgen before coming to Paris about 1775. He was made a master in 1778. Weisweiler usually employed plain veneers combined with gilt bronze mounts of high quality. The most distinctive feature of his furniture is the interlaced stretchers of complex design which he often employed. Unlike many of his contemporaries, Weisweiler continued working into the Napoleonic era.

Wood and wood veneer with gilt bronze mounts and marble top, 36 inches high, 58-1/2 inches wide, 19-1/2 inches deep. Stamped twice (on back): Weisweiler. Executed ca.1780–1790.
Collections: Duchess of Angoulême; Jean Deschamps; Henry Deschamps.
Literature: William M. Milliken, "New Accessions of French Furniture," CMA *Bulletin*, IX (July 1922), 114-119.

The Cleveland Museum of Art, Given Anonymously

Martin Carlin

Died Paris 1785

Carlin was made a master in 1766. He worked largely for dealers in furnishings, rather than directly for private patrons. His furniture is distinctive in style and characterized by the use of exotic decorative materials, such as Oriental lacquer and Sèvres porcelain.

60 Worktable

Wood marquetry with Sèvres porcelain top and gilt bronze mounts, 30-1/2 inches high, 17 inches in diameter. Remains of Carlin's stamp and "JME" mark beneath porcelain top. Executed ca.1775–1785.
Collections: Alfred de Rothschild; Lady Carnarvon; John L. Severance.
Literature: Catalogue of the John L. Severance Collection (Cleveland, 1942), p. 45, no. 87, pl. XXII. [Jean Meuvret], *Les Ebénistes du XVIIIᵉ siècle Français* (Paris, 1963), pp. 250-251, fig. 1.

The Cleveland Museum of Art
The John L. Severance Collection

Jean-Baptiste Sené

Paris 1748—Paris 1803

Sené was the product of a long family tradition of chairmaking. After Jacob, he was the most important chairmaker of the Louis XVI period. He was made a master in 1769. He received numerous royal commissions and produced some of his best work for the use of Marie-Antoinette.

61 Pair of Stools

Carved and gilded wood with modern upholstery, 17-5/8 inches high, 28-1/8 inches wide, 20-5/16 inches deep. Each stool inscribed twice (inside cross piece): "N° 35" and "N° 37" respectively.
Collection: Marie-Antoinette at Compiègne.
Literature: Pierre Verlet, *French Royal Furniture* (London, 1963), pp. 175-176, no. 35, figs. 35b, 35c.
On May 1, 1786, forty *pliants* (folding stools) were ordered from Hauré for Marie-Antoinette's Salon des Jeux at Compiègne. Twenty-four *pliants* were sent to Fontainebleau for the Queen's Salon des Jeux there. On September 3, 1786, twenty-four additional *pliants* were ordered to complete the set at Compiègne. Because of the numbers they bear, the Cleveland stools were probably included in the latter group. The frames for these stools were made by Sené, the carving was by Vallois under Hauré's supervision, and the gilding on a white ground was by Chatard. Capin supplied the upholstery. The present upholstery is a modern reproduction of the original. The stools have also been regilded.

The Cleveland Museum of Art
The John L. Severance Fund

62 Pair of Firedogs

Anonymous, France

Gilt bronze, 18-1/4 inches high, and 19-13/16 inches high. Executed ca.1785.

Collection: Marquis of Hertford, Paris; Mrs. Elisabeth Severance Prentiss, Cleveland.

Literature: Catalogue of the Elisabeth Severance Prentiss Collection (Cleveland, 1944), p. 61, nos. 42-43, pl. XXVIII. There is some confusion about the attribution of these firedogs. They seem certainly to have been cast from the same molds as an almost identical pair in France. There is apparently only one pair in France, which was originally published as in the Mobilier National, later in the Louvre, and most recently at Versailles. Emile Molinier, *Le Mobilier au XVIIe et au XVIIIe siècle* (Paris, n.d.), pp. 215–216, identifies the pair in France with ones made in 1786 for Marie-Antoinette. Boizot and Thomire were the chief artists engaged in making them. At The Art Institute of Chicago, Treasures of Versailles, 1962, a pair of firedogs were exhibited (no. 156) which are probably identical with those published by Molinier. In the catalogue of the exhibition in Chicago they are identified with a pair made in 1784 for the private apartments of Marie-Antoinette on the ground floor of the main building of Versailles and are attributed to "Pitoin(?)". The pair of firedogs in Cleveland were formerly attributed by the Museum to Boizot and Thomire.

The Cleveland Museum of Art
The Elisabeth Severance Prentiss Collection

Pierre Gouthière

Bar-sur-Aube 1732—Paris 1813/14

With his younger contemporary, Thomire, Gouthière is the most famous *ciseleur*, or finisher of cast bronzes, active in France in the last half of the eighteenth century. He is one of the few craftsmen of the period to have won sufficient renown in his lifetime to be occasionally mentioned by name in contemporary catalogues of sales. He came first to Paris in 1758. By the 1760's his reputation was firmly established and he was working for the most exalted patrons in France. His work was particularly popular with Marie-Antoinette.

63 Pair of Firedogs in the Form of Goats

Attributed to Pierre Gouthière

Gilt bronze, 17-5/16 inches high. Executed ca.1780.
Literature: Edwin J. Hipkiss, *Handbook of the Department of Decorative Arts of Europe and America* (Boston, 1928), exhibition 11.
The pair of firedogs was among the objects bought by Colonel James Swan at the French government sales held just after the Revolution. They were brought by him to Boston.

The Museum of Fine Arts, Boston
Swan Collection, Bequest of Miss Elizabeth Howard Bartol

64

63

64 Vase (one of a pair) with Mounts (by Thomire?)

Anonymous, Sèvres Factory, France

Porcelain and gilt bronze, 17-1/8 inches high. Executed ca.1784.

Collection: Mme. Charcot Hendry, London.

The form and mounts of the present vase closely resemble those of a pair of vases now at Windsor Castle which are dated 1782. Pierre Verlet, "Orders for Sèvres from the French Court," *The Burlington Magazine*, XCVI (July 1954), 202-206, fig. 18, has associated the mounts of the Windsor vases with a memorandum by Thomire which reads: "20 September 1784./Garniture de vases à bouc, fonte, modèle en cire, monture, dorure au mat. . . . 1.500."

The Walters Art Gallery, Baltimore

65 Rectangular Box

Anonymous, France

Gold with *en plein* enamel *en grisaille* in grey-green, 1-3/4 inches high, 3-1/4 inches wide, 2-5/16 inches deep. Maker's mark partially erased and unidentified. Executed 1768–1769(?).

The Cleveland Museum of Art
Gift of Mrs. Edward B. Greene

Pierre Marie Gault de Saint-Germain

Paris 1754—Paris 1842

Though "De Gault," as he usually signed his name, is primarily noted as a miniature painter, he also painted full-scale pictures, several of which were exhibited in the Paris Salons of various years. He became a member of the Academie de St.-Luc as a miniature painter in 1774. In the early nineteenth century he published several books on art.

66 Oval Box with Six Miniatures Based upon Le Brun's Paintings of the Life of Alexander

Gouache miniatures *en grisaille* on card mounted *à cage* in a framework of tooled gold and blue enamel, 1-5/16 inches high. Signed (cover miniature, lower right) : . . . De Gault. Inscribed (cover miniature, lower left): L. B. v. Dated: 1779–1780(?).

Collection: Comte Gregoire Stroganoff (*Catalogue*, II [Rome, 1912], 216).

The Cleveland Museum of Art
Gift of Mrs. Edward B. Greene

67 *A Bacchanal*

Anonymous, France

Wax relief, 16 inches wide. Executed ca.1785.
Collection: J. P. Morgan (Sale, Parke-Bernet Galleries,
Inc., New York, March 22-25, 1944, no. 679).
The relief was formerly attributed by the Museum to
Claude Michel, called Clodion. Several other wax reliefs
of the same composition, also attributed to Clodion, exist.
See Sale, Palais de San Donato, Catalogue, 1880, no. 1424;
and Gaston Migeon, "Les Accroissements des Musées—
Musée du Louvre," *Les Arts* (April 1908), 10-15. Stanislas
Lami, *Dictionnaire des Sculpteurs de l'Ecole Française au
Dix-Huitième Siècle*, II (Paris, 1911), 157, records a
Jeux de bacchantes, signed by Clodion and dated 1784,
which passed in Muhlbacher Sale, May, 1907. The latter
might be related in composition to the present relief. In
the Musée des Arts Décoratifs, Paris, there is a drawing of
a very similar composition signed "Moitte Sculpteur 1785."
In style the present relief seems to have more to do with
Moitte than Clodion, but Moitte is not recorded as having
made wax reliefs, and this relief might well have been
executed by an anonymous sculptor after his design.

The Cleveland Museum of Art
Purchase from the J. H. Wade Fund

Camille de Pernon

Camille de Pernon was a silkmaker active at Lyon. In
1787 Marie-Antoinette commissioned from him textiles for her private apartments at the Petit Trianon.
They remained incomplete at the time of the Revolution. He made hangings for Josephine's Petit Salon at
Saint-Cloud. In 1804 his firm became Pernon and
Grand.

68 Textile Hanging

Silk in diaper weave with embroidery, 80 x 22-1/2 inches.
Executed ca.1790.
Figures similar to that in the central medallion of the pres-
ent hanging occur in textiles made by Pernon for Saint-
Cloud under the Consulate. See Paul Lafond, *L'Art
Décoratif et le Mobilier Sous la République et l'Empire*
(Paris, 1906), p. 125.

The Cleveland Museum of Art
Purchase from the J. H. Wade Fund

69 *Hercules with the Skin of the Nemean Lion*

Anonymous, Höchst Factory near Mainz, Germany

Porcelain decorated with enamel colors, 11-1/2 inches high. Mark: Wheel with Electorial Hat in blue. Executed 1765–1774.

Collection: J. P. Morgan, New York (given in 1917).

Wadsworth Atheneum, Hartford, J. P. Morgan Collection

(Jacob) Philipp Hackert

*Prenzlau 1737—San Piero di Careggio
near Florence 1807*

From 1753 to 1755, Hackert studied with his father, who was a portrait painter. He then entered the Berlin Academy. He was strongly influenced by later seventeenth-century Dutch landscape painting and by Claude. In the early 1760's he traveled around Germany and in 1765 was in Paris. With his brother, Hackert went to Rome in 1768. Much of his work done there was for English patrons, but he also worked for Katherine II of Russia and Ferdinand IV of Naples. He was a prolific and popular painter.

70 *Landscape with a Ruined Castle*

Oil on canvas, 23 x 32 inches.
Collection: Edith J. Freeman, Detroit.
Exhibited: Detroit Institute of Arts, German Paintings and Drawings from the Time of Goethe in American Collections, 1949, no. 34; catalogue published in *Art Quarterly*, XII (1949), p. 238.

Dr. and Mrs. Albert Cohen, Ann Arbor, Michigan

Franz Kobell

Mannheim 1749—Munich 1822

Franz Kobell probably received his earliest training from his brother, Ferdinand, but their styles are quite different. Franz was in Rome from 1779 to 1784. He was influenced by Claude and Poussin through Vernet. Though he produced only a few paintings, he is said to have made more than 10,000 sepia landscape drawings.

71 *A Romantic Landscape*

Pen and sepia wash, on white paper, 14-1/8 x 20-3/4 inches. Inscribed (on mount): Franz Kobell del.
Collections: John Witt Randall; Belinda L. Randall.
Literature: Agnes Mongan and Paul J. Sachs, *Drawings in the Fogg Museum of Art*, I (Cambridge, Mass., 1940), 214-215, no. 420; III, fig. 211.

Fogg Art Museum, Harvard University
Bequest of Belinda L. Randall
from the John Witt Randall Collection

72 Covered Vase

Anonymous, Fürstenberg Factory, Brunswick, Germany

Porcelain decorated with gold and enamel colors, 15 inches high. Mark: FG4 in cursive script in underglaze blue. Executed ca.1780.

The mark "FG4" stands for Fürstenberg, model G4. A vase of this model is illustrated in Christian Scherer, *Das Fürstenberger Porzellan* (Berlin, 1909), p. 164, fig. 129. It was copied from a Wedgwood model.

The Art Institute of Chicago

73 Urn

W. S. (unidentified), Vienna

Silver with ivory knop on spigot, 14-1/4 inches high.
Marks: Maker's mark "W.S." (unidentified) punched
three times. Vienna mark with date 1798 punched three
times. Dated 1798.

Mr. and Mrs. Heinz Schneider, Cleveland

Angelica Kauffmann

Chur 1741—Rome 1807

Angelica Kauffmann was Swiss by birth. In 1763 she
went to Rome to study painting. By 1766 she was in
London. There she became a friend of Reynolds and
a founding member of the Royal Academy. She established a successful practice as a portrait painter, and
her history pictures were popularized through engravings. In 1781 she married Antonio Zucchi, and the
two of them returned to Rome.

74 *Praxiteles Giving Phryne His Statue of Cupid*

Oil on canvas, 16-7/8 x 18-3/4 inches. Signed and dated
(upper right): Angelica Kauffman/Pinx. Romae/1794.
Collection: George Bowles, Esq., The Grove, Wanstead,
England; C. F. Rushout, Sezincourt, England, a collateral

descendant of Mr. Bowles (Sale, London, Phillips and Neale's, 1879).

Literature: G. G. de Rossi, *Vita di Angelica Kauffmann* (Florence, 1810), p. 81. Frances A. Gerard, *Angelica Kauffmann* (New York, 1893), p. 281. Lady Victoria Manners and Dr. George C. Williamson, *Angelica Kauffmann, R. A.* (New York, 1924), p. 164. Anthony M. Clark, "Five Roman Masters of the Settecento," RISD *Museum Notes,* XLV (May 1959), 6, 8, fig. 7.

The base of the statue of Cupid is signed Praxiteles. The present picture is one of a set of four which Angelica Kauffmann painted for George Bowles.

Museum of Art, Rhode Island School of Design

75 *Judgment of Paris*

Oil on canvas, 31-1/2 x 39-1/2 inches. Signed (lower left): ANGELICA KAUFFMAN Pinx. Executed ca.1780.

Collections: Alfred Beit, Esq., London; R. Brooman White, Esq., Dumbartonshire; Samuel Katz, Port Chester, New York.

Exhibited: London, Royal Academy, 1781, no. 153.

Literature: Frances A. Gerard, *Angelica Kauffmann* (London, 1892), p. 171. Lady Victoria Manners and Dr. George C. Williamson, *Angelica Kauffmann, R. A.* (London, 1924), p. 178.

Engraved by F. Bartolozzi, 1798.

Ponce Museum of Art, Puerto Rico
Luis A. Ferré Foundation

Benjamin West

Springfield, Pennsylvania 1738—London 1820

West learned "the mechanical part" of painting in America before going to Rome in 1760. There he was in close contact with the circle of Mengs and Hamilton. West set himself up as a portrait painter in London in 1763. In 1768 he was introduced to George III, beginning his long association with the Crown. He was a founder-member of the Royal Academy, where he exhibited in 1771 his most famous work, *Death of Wolfe.* West succeeded Reynolds as President of the Royal Academy in 1792, but refused knighthood because of his Quaker principles.

76 *Agrippina Landing at Brundisium with the Ashes of Germanicus*

Oil on canvas, 64-1/2 x 94-1/2 inches. Signed and dated (lower center): B. WEST PINTIX: 1768.
Collections: Archbishop Drummond; Lord Kinnoul.
Literature: John Galt, *The Life, Studies, and Works of Benjamin West, Esq. . . .* (London, 1820), p. 225. Ellis Waterhouse, *Painting in Britain 1530–1790* (Harmondsworth, Middlesex, 1953), p. 201. Grose Evans, *Benjamin West and the Taste of his Times* (Carbondale, Illinois, 1959), pp. 5, 21, 44, 50, 52, 54, pl. I. Robert Rosenblum, "Review of Grose Evans' *Benjamin West and the Taste of his Times*," *Art Bulletin,* XLII (March 1960), 76.
The first of three pictures which West painted of the subject. There was also a sketch in oil on paper. The picture was commissioned by Archbishop Drummond. West's long association with George III began when Archbishop Drummond showed this picture to the king.

Yale University Art Gallery, Gift of Louis M. Rabinowitz

77 Etruria

Oil on paper, mounted on panel, 20-1/8 x 25-1/2 inches.
Signed and dated (bottom center): B. West, 1791.
Collections: Mrs. S. J. Tuttle; William MacBeth.
Exhibited: Allentown (Pennsylvania) Art Museum, The
World of Benjamin West, 1962, p. 64, no. 97.
Literature: Gardern Teall, "Benjamin West's *Etruria*,"
International Studio, LXXXIX (January 1928), 45-46. *Old
Wedgwood,* no. 6 (1939), pp. 64, 71-72. Jean Gorely,
"Josiah Wedgwood and the Museum in the 18th-century
World," *American Collector,* XVII (June 1948), 15, fig. 8.
Virgil Barker, *American Painting: History and Interpre-
tation* (New York, 1950), p. 204.

May be associated with decorations which West made for
Queen's Lodge, Windsor, in particular a picture described
as "Genius calling forth the Fine Arts to adorn Manufac-
tures and Commerce, and recording the names of eminent
men in those pursuits." See John Galt, *The Life . . . of
Benjamin West, Esq. . . .* (London, 1820), pp. 214, 217.
The two boys in the foreground hold a representation of
one of Wedgwood's copies after the Portland Vase.

The Cleveland Museum of Art, John Huntington Collection

78 Antiochus and Stratonice

Pen and ink with sepia and white washes, 17-1/2 x 23-3/8
inches. Signed and dated (bottom, left of center): B. W.
1773(?).
Collection: Robert Frank, London.
Literature: John Galt, *The Life, Studies, and Works of
Benjamin West, Esq. . . .* (London, 1820), p. 226. H. Stew-
art Leonard, "Benjamin West's Antiochus and Stratonice,"
CAMSL *Bulletin,* XXXVI (1951), 48-50. Wolfgang Ste-
chow, "Antiochus and Stratonice," *News and Notes, The
Art Gallery of Toronto* (May 1962).

City Art Museum of St. Louis

79 *The Grecian Daughter Defending Her Father*

Oil on panel, 19 x 23 inches. Signed and dated (upper right): B. West 1794.
Collections: Painted for George Bowles, The Grove, Wanstead; Mr. Harding (?).
Exhibited: Allentown (Pennsylvania) Art Museum, The World of Benjamin West, 1962, p. 59, no. 22.
The subject was presumably taken from a play by Arthur Murphy.

The Newark Museum

George Romney

Dalton-le-Furness 1734—Kendal 1802

Romney was a very fashionable portrait painter and, after Reynolds and Gainsborough, the best practitioner of that genre in the England of his day. He came to London in 1762, made a brief trip to Paris in 1764, and was in Italy from 1773 to 1775. As with so many English artists of his generation, Romney had an ambition to create history pictures, but patronage for such work was almost totally lacking. A result of this frustrated ambition was a large number of drawings in which both Neo-classicism and Romney's rather odd character found expression.

80 *Sidonian Recollections*

Oil on canvas, 26-1/2 x 23-1/4 inches. Inscribed (lower right): Sidonian Recollections. Painted ca.1783–1785.
Collections: Sale, Christie's, London, March 28, 1924, no. 12; Goole; New York art market 1945, 1962.
Exhibited: Northampton, Mass., Smith College Museum of Art, The Drawings of George Romney, 1962, no. 109.
Literature: F. Saxl and R. Wittkower, *British Art and the Mediterranean* (London, 1948), p. 82, no. 3.
A representation of the famous actress, Mrs. Sarah Siddons, as three classical tragic masks.

Mr. and Mrs. Thomas J. McCormick, Poughkeepsie

81 *Captive or Dejected Lady;*
   Possibly Andromache

Pen in dark brown-black ink over faint charcoal, 20-1/4 x
12-3/4 inches. Stamped: (upper left), George Romney
(applied ca.1937); (lower right), G Romney (applied ca.
1937).

Collections: Xavier Haas and his heirs, Paris, until 1959;
Mr. and Mrs. J. Richardson Dilworth, Jr.
Exhibited: Northampton, Mass., Smith College Museum of
Art, The Drawings of George Romney, 1962, no. 9, pl. XXV.

Yale University Art Gallery
Gift of Mr. and Mrs. J. Richardson Dilworth, B.A., 1938

John Hoppner

London 1758—London 1810

Hoppner was a successful portrait painter in his day. He was appointed portrait painter to the Prince of Wales in 1789 and was made a member of the Royal Academy in 1795. His style was not, however, very original. He borrowed ideas and techniques from all his famous English contemporaries.

Oil on canvas, 50 x 40-1/2 inches. Painted ca.1784–85.
Collections: Lord Hampden, London; English private collector.
Exhibited: London, Royal Academy, 1785, no. 99.
Literature: H. P. K. Skipton, *John Hoppner* (London, 1905), p. 166. Algernon Graves, *The Royal Academy of Arts*, IV (London, 1906), 153. William McKay and W. Roberts, *John Hoppner, R. A.* (London, 1909), p. 302. Engraved in mezzotint by Valentine Green, July 1, 1798.

Newhouse Galleries, New York

Frankfurt 1734/35—London 1810

A German by birth, Zoffany spent a long period of time in Rome as a youth. He arrived in London about 1760 with a neat, polished, and highly-finished style which he employed in often small-scale pictures. His work was especially admired by George III. He was in Florence from 1772 to 1776 and in India from 1783 to 1789. It was Zoffany's skill at depicting the world about him in surprising detail which won for him contemporary popularity and still arouses admiration today.

83 *Charles Towneley, Esquire, and His Friends in the Towneley Gallery, Park Street, Westminster*

Oil on canvas, 50 x 40 inches. Painted ca.1790.
Collections: Charles Towneley; Lord O'Hagen; bought by Burnley Corporation at Christie's, London, 1939.
Exhibited: London, Royal Academy, 1790, no. 191.
Literature: Algernon Graves, *A Century of Loan Exhibitions, 1813–1912,* IV (London, 1913), 1747. Lady Victoria Manners and Dr. George C. Williamson, *John Zoffany, R. A., His Life and Works* (London and New York, 1920), pp. 121-123. Sacheverell Sitwell, *Conversation Pieces* (London, 1937), pp. 33-34; fig. 37.

Charles Towneley was an important collector of ancient art. Many of the sculptures depicted in the present picture are now in the British Museum.

Towneley Hall, Art Gallery and Museum, Burnley, England

James Stuart

London 1713–London 1788

As early as 1748, when James Stuart and Nicholas
Revett were in Naples, they laid plans to go to Athens
in order to describe and portray its monuments. They
left for Greece in 1751, and did not return to England until 1755. The first volume of their book, *The
Antiquities of Athens*, appeared in 1762, the second
in 1789, and the third in 1795. Both Stuart and Revett
practiced as architects after their return to England,
incorporating into their designs motifs which they
had seen in Greece, but their publication remains
their most important achievement.

84 *View of the Incantada, Thessalonica, Greece*

Gouache on paper, mounted, 12-1/2 x 18 inches. Executed
1751–1754.
Collection: W. Thomas Howard, presented 1783.
This gouache was intended for publication in Stuart and
Revett's *The Antiquities of Athens*. It did appear in volume III, chapter IX, plate I of that work, but that volume
was produced by Willey Reveley in 1795, several years
after Stuart's death.

Royal Institute of British Architects, London

William Chambers

Gothenburg 1723—London 1796

Chambers was born in Sweden of English parents. As a youth, he sailed to China with the Swedish East India Company. From this journey came a publication on Chinese architecture and some Chinese garden ornaments, notably the pagoda in Kew Gardens. In 1749 Chambers went to Paris, where he studied architecture under Blondel and became acquainted with some of the important French architects of his generation. His style was to retain a French flavor throughout his life. By 1750 he was in Italy, where he knew Clérisseau in Rome. He returned to England in 1755. Shortly thereafter he became architectural tutor to the Prince of Wales. It was in part as a result of this association that Chambers became the important official architect of his generation. Chambers' style was in essence Palladianism modified by elements drawn from early French Neoclassicism and his own refined taste.

86 Design for a Royal Palace

Pen and wash, 16-7/8 x 48-1/4 inches. Executed ca.1775. Chambers attempted unsuccessfully to persuade George III to build a new royal palace in London. This drawing represents his last scheme for such a building.

Royal Institute of British Architects, London

85 Design for a Wall Mirror

Pen and ink with water color, 18-1/2 x 9-1/2 inches. Inscribed (on verso): Adderbury. Executed ca.1765.
Literature: John Harris, "Some English Architectural and Decorative Drawings," MMA *Bulletin*, XXI (February 1963), 217, fig. 4.

The Metropolitan Museum of Art, Dick Fund, 1934

Antonio Zucchi

Venice 1726—Rome 1795

Zucchi was a member of a prominent North Italian family of artists. He was a pupil of Fontabasso and Amigoni. Zucchi became associated with Clérisseau and Robert Adam when they were in Venice preparing the drawings made at Spalatro for publication. About 1766 Zucchi went to London, where he was occupied chiefly in supplying pictures for Adam's designs for decorations. He became an associate of the Royal Academy in 1770. He married the painter Angelica Kauffmann in London in 1781, and shortly thereafter they returned to Italy.

87 *An Architectural Allegory*

Oil on canvas, *en grisaille*, 28 x 23-1/4 inches. Painted ca.1778.

Collections: Robert Adam (Sale, Christie's, London, May 20, 1818, no. 5); Richard Cosway, ca.1818–ca.1820; Sir Jeffry Wyattville, presented by him to the R.I.B.A. sometime after 1830.

The subject of the allegory can be thus described: "A student conducted to Minerva, who points to Greece, and Italy, as the countries from whence he must derive the most perfect knowledge and Taste in elegant Architecture." As engraved by Bartolozzi, the composition of the present picture served as the frontispiece for volume I of Robert and James Adam's *The Works in Architecture*, published in 1778. For many years the painting was attributed to Angelica Kauffmann.

Royal Institute of British Architects, London

Robert Adam

Edinburgh 1728—London 1792

Adam was the son of William Adam, a Scottish architect of some accomplishment. From an early time, Adam had ambitions to be an innovator in architecture, not just a competent provincial practitioner as his father had been. He therefore went to Italy to perfect his talents. Adam's chief mentor was the young French architect and draughtsman, Clérisseau, who both instructed him in architectural rendering and helped him make views of the Palace of Diocletian at Spalatro. The publication of the latter was significant in establishing Adam's reputation in England. While in Italy, Adam also knew Piranesi. He set up practice in London in 1759, and within two years he had made fashionable the early Neo-classic style with which he had returned from Italy. Adam's work as an architect was largely confined to the remodeling of existing structures. He had many assistants and was able to provide consistent interior designs, complete to the smallest detail.

89 Door Furniture

Brass, 5-1/4 x 9-3/8 inches. Executed ca.1765.
Collection: Sale, Christie's, London, October 7, 1924, no. 30.
Resembles very closely examples from Lansdowne House, London. See James Lees-Milne, *The Age of Adam* (London, 1947), figs. 51, 52.

City Art Museum of St. Louis

88 Armchair

Carved and gilded wood, upholstered in tapestry, 38 inches high. Executed 1765–1770.
Collections: Made for Sir Lawrence Dundas, Moor Park; Dundas Family, 19 Arlington Street, London, and Aske Hall, until 1934 (Sale, Christie's, London, *Tapestry, Furniture and Porcelain . . . of . . . the Marquess of Zetland,* April 26, 1934); Mr. and Mrs. George Horace Lorimer, Philadelphia.
Literature: Fiske Kimball, "The Moor Park Tapestry Suite of Furniture by Robert Adam," PMA *Bulletin,* XXXVI (March 1941).
The chair frame was constructed by Samuel Norman of Whitehall, London. The tapestry cover was made at the Gobelins factory which was then under the direction of Jacques Neilson.

Philadelphia Museum of Art

90 Design for a Ceiling
at 7 Queen Street, Edinburgh

Pen and water color, 18-3/4 x 24 inches. Signed and dated
(lower left): Rt Adam Archt. 1770. Inscribed (above):
Design of a Ceiling for the 2ᵈ. Drawing Room, for Lord
Chief Baron Ord.

Royal Institute of British Architects, London

London 1741—London 1825

Dance was the son of a successful architect who had
specialized in rather untutored Palladian designs for
the merchants of London. The younger Dance went
to Italy in 1758 and remained there for five years.
When he returned to England, he brought with him a
more advanced version of early Neo-classic architecture than that practiced by Adam or Chambers, since
in Dance's designs, form, as well as decoration, was
of a decidedly Neo-classic character. Dance built
comparatively few buildings, and several of them
have not survived, but it is evident that he was an
architect of considerable talent and originality. In
his last works, Dance moved into the second phase of
the Neo-classic style in architecture—for example, in
his use of a purely Greek Doric portico for a country
house design.

91 Design for All Hallow's, London

Pen and wash, 15-3/4 x 19-1/4 inches. Executed ca.1765.
All Hallow's was the first structure designed by Dance
after his return from Italy in 1765. It was constructed
between 1765 and 1768.

Royal Institute of British Architects, London

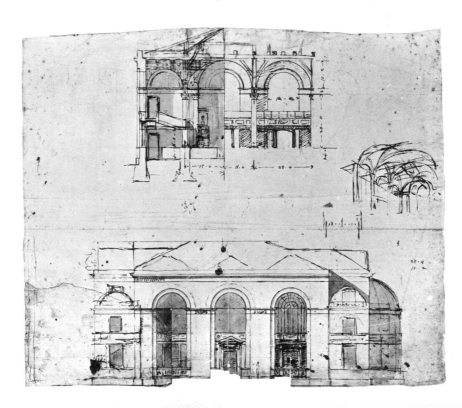

James Wyatt

Burton Constable 1746—near Marlborough 1813

Wyatt was an extremely successful and popular architect. He rivaled the brothers Adam when they were at the height of their fame, and he became surveyor-general when Chambers died in 1796. He had no personal style, however, and was merely a clever adapter of other men's ideas. His Neo-classic buildings were close in style to Adam's, but he was more famous for his Gothic country houses.

92 Design for a House

Pen and water color, 19-1/2 x 27-7/8 inches. Signed and dated (lower left): James Wyatt Arc/April. 1771.
Exhibited: London, Royal Academy, 1771, no. 228(?).
Literature: Anthony Dale, *James Wyatt* (Oxford, 1956), pl. I.
Wyatt's earliest surviving design for a country house. It reflects his Neo-classic training in Italy, first in Venice under Antonio Visentini, and later in Rome where he passed the years from 1764 to 1768.

Royal Institute of British Architects, London

Michelangelo Pergolesi

Pergolesi was one of the Italian artists whom Robert Adam brought to London to assist him in carrying out his designs for interior decorations. Pergolesi's most important work was a collection of designs published under the title *Designs for Various Ornaments,* . . . between 1777 and 1801.

93 Design for a Ceiling

In the Manner of Pergolesi
Water color, 5 x 13-7/8 inches. Executed ca.1775–1780.
The Metropolitan Museum of Art, Dick Fund, 1934

Thomas Heming

Active London after 1745

Thomas Heming seems to have been one of the most important London silversmiths of his time. His trade card carried the legend "Goldsmith to his Majesty" and the Royal Arms. Among his recorded works is an alms bowl which the king gave to Trinity Church, New York, in 1766. Thomas Heming was one of several silversmiths of that name active in London in the last half of the eighteenth century. The firm which he founded survived into the twentieth century as Messrs. Hemming & Co. Ltd., 28 Conduit Street.

94 Tea Urn

Silver, 17-1/2 inches high. Marks: Leopard's Head, Lion Passant, TH crowned, date letter "b." Executed 1777–1778.
Collection: James Hazen Hyde.
Exhibited: The Cooper Union Museum, The Four Continents, 1961, no. 90.
Atlas holds up a globe. Around it are attached four medallions with allegorical figures of the four continents.

The Cooper Union Museum, New York

Josiah Wedgwood

Burslem 1730—Etruria 1795

Josiah Wedgwood was born into a family which for several generations had been engaged in making ceramics. At an early age he himself learned the trade. About 1755 he became associated with Thomas Whieldon, one of the cleverest potters in Staffordshire, from whom he undoubtedly learned much. In 1759 Wedgwood established his own pottery in Burslem. In 1762 he gained royal patronage, which added greatly to his reputation. It was just after that date that Wedgwood turned his attention to making the decorative ceramics upon which his fame rests. In 1768 he entered into a partnership with Thomas Bentley, who managed the London sales of the firm, and in the following year they opened the new works called Etruria, near Hanley. Among the many artists whom Wedgwood employed, the most famous is John Flaxman.

95 Bust, Copy of the Medici Venus

Polished basalt ware, 22-1/8 inches high. Mark: Wedgwood and Bentley. Executed ca.1769–1780.
The artists who participated in making the copy of the Medici Venus were Hackwood and Hoskins & Grant.

The Museum of Fine Arts, Boston
Gift of Miss Elizabeth Day McCormick

96 Vase

Basalt ware with painted decorations in red and white, 11-1/4 inches high. Mark: "Wedgwood" impressed on bottom. Executed 1769–1780.
Literature: Ross E. Taggert (ed.), *The Frank P. and Harriet C. Burnap Collection of English Pottery* (Kansas City, 1953), p. 84, no. 453, pl. top left.
This vase is an imitation of ancient Apulia ware

Nelson Gallery—Atkins Museum, Kansas City
Burnap Collection

97 Apsley Pellott-Rickman Copy of the Portland Vase (#7)

Black and white jaspar ware, 10 inches high. Stamped (inside neck): No. 7. Executed ca.1790.
Literature: Two monographs are concerned with the Portland Vase and its Wedgwood copies: Wolf Mankowitz,

The Portland Vase and the Wedgwood Copies (London, 1952); Erika Simon, *Die Portlandvase* (Mainz, 1957).
The artists who contributed to the project of copying the Portland Vase were Josiah Wedgwood, Josiah Wedgwood II, Hackwood, Webber, and William Wood.
The Museum of Fine Arts, Boston, Gift of Lloyd E. Hawes

Giuseppe Cades

Rome 1750—Rome 1799

Cades was born in Rome of a French father. He studied under Corvi, and in 1766 won first prize at the Accademia di San Luca. Cades made copies of old masters in Rome and Florence, chiefly for English and German patrons. In 1786 he was made a member of the Accademia di San Luca. He was patronized by Katherine II of Russia. In his last years Cades was influenced by David.

99 *Bacchus Abandoning Ariadne*

Black ink, bistre washes, on white paper, 13-1/2 x 17-1/4 inches. Executed ca.1780.

Anthony M. Clark, Minneapolis

98 *The Meeting of Gautier, Count of Antwerp, and His Daughter, Violante*

Oil on canvas, 14-5/8 x 27-1/2 inches. Painted 1787.
Collection: Private collection, France.
Exhibited: Rome, Palazzo delle Esposizioni, Il Settecento a Roma, 1959, p. 72, no. 113, pl. 28.
Literature: AIC *Quarterly,* LVII (Winter 1963–1964), illustrated, p. 4.
The subject is drawn from *The Decameron* of Boccaccio. It is one of several extant sketches for a ceiling decoration commissioned in 1787 by Marc'Antonio Borghese for a room in the Villa Borghese. This decoration is Cades' most famous composition.

The Art Institute of Chicago, Worcester Sketch Fund

Tomasso Conca

Gaeta ca.1750—Rome 1815

Tomasso was the nephew and pupil of Sebastiano Conca. He became a member of the Accademia di San Luca in 1773 and Princeps in 1793. From his uncle he learned a late Baroque style, but he soon came under the influence of Mengs. He executed decorations in the Casino of the Villa Borghese, the Museo Pio-Clementino, and the cathedral of Città di Castello.

100 Sketch for a Memorial to Marchesa Rondanini

Red and black chalks, with red wash, heightened with white, 12-1/2 x 9 inches. Signed (lower left): Tomas/ Conca. Executed probably before 1808.
Collection: Robert Gilmor, purchased Rome, 1843.
Literature: Anthony M. Clark, "Roman Eighteenth-century Drawings in the Gilmor Collection," BMA *News*, XXIV (Spring 1961), 5-12, fig. 8.

Baltimore Museum of Art, Robert Gilmor Collection
On permanent loan from the Peabody Institute, Baltimore

101 *Achilles and Patroclus*

Anonymous, Italy or France

Oil on canvas, 23 x 38 inches. Painted ca.1780.
The owner of this picture has suggested that it be attributed to a follower of Vien. Anthony M. Clark has proposed that it be given to Thaddäus Kuntz, an artist who worked in Rome from about 1750 to 1793.

Denys Sutton, Esq., London

Joseph Platzer

Prague 1751—Vienna 1806

Platzer, who had been a pupil of Franz Wolf in Prague, divided his time between Vienna and Prague, working primarily as a designer of theatre decors. In that capacity he executed commissions for both public theatres and private patrons. He was made a member of the Vienna Academy in 1789, and in 1795 was appointed Kammermaler to the emperor.

102 *The Interior of a Fortress*

Pen, sepia and grey wash, 8-11/16 x 12-1/2 inches.
Collections: Mayr-Fajt; Scholz.
Exhibited: Minneapolis Institute of Art, Theater Drawings from the Donald Oenslager Collection, 1963, no. 55. Catalogue: MIA *Bulletin*, LII (March 1963), 33.
Literature: George Freedley, *Theatrical Designs from the Baroque through Neoclassicism*, II (New York, 1940), pl. 20.

Donald Oenslager, New York

Giuseppe Boschi

Rome ca.1760—after 1808

In 1783 Boschi won a first prize of the second class at the Accademia di San Luca in Rome. From at least 1795 he was engaged in making bronze reductions of antique sculptures. In 1800 and 1801 he was arrested for keeping a silversmith's workshop without a license. In 1806 he was admitted to the silversmith's guild as a master. He continued making small bronzes after that date.

103 *Bacchus and Ariadne*

Bronze, 21-3/4 inches high. Signed (on base): G. Boschi. Executed ca.1790–1800.
Literature: Hugh Honour, "After the Antique: Some Italian Bronzes of the Eighteenth Century," *Apollo,* LXXVII (March 1963), 194-200, fig. 10.
Reproduces an ancient sculpture which was known in the eighteenth century as the Marbury Hall *Bacchus and Ariadne.*

The Minneapolis Institute of Arts

Giacomo & Giovanni Zoffoli

ca.1731—Rome 1785
ca.1745—Rome 1805

The lives and works of the brothers Zoffoli remain somewhat obscure. Giacomo, who was a silversmith by training, seems to have instigated a flourishing trade in small bronze replicas of ancient sculptures. It was continued after his death by his brother, Giovanni. There is evidence that on at least one occasion Giacomo paid a sculptor, Vincenzo Pacetti, to copy an ancient sculpture. It seems likely that the brothers Zoffoli relied upon others for the models from which their bronzes were cast.

104 *Seated Roman Matron* (the so-called *Agrippina*)

Giacomo or Giovanni Zoffoli

Bronze, 10-3/4 inches high. Signed (right side of base): G. Zoffoli.
Literature: Hugh Honour, "Bronze Statuettes by Giacomo and Giovanni Zoffoli," *The Connoisseur*, CXLVIII (November 1961), 198-205, fig. 1.
Copied from a marble sculpture formerly in the Farnese Collection, now in the Naples Museum.

Anthony M. Clark, Minneapolis

Giuseppe Maggiolini

106 Armchair

Anonymous, Italy

Carved, painted, and gilded wood, 36 inches high. Executed ca.1800.

The Art Institute of Chicago
Gift of Cornelius Crane and Florence C. Belosselsky

Parabiago 1738—Parabiago 1814

Maggiolini is one of the most famous Italian furniture makers of the eighteenth century. He was active in Milan, where he worked for Ferdinand of Austria, Governor of Lombardy, and his wife, Maria Beatrix d'Este. In form his furniture reflects French styles and is characterized by elaborate marquetry inlays.

105 Pair of Cabinets

Veneered wood with marble tops, 35-1/2 inches high. Executed ca.1790–1800.

The commode, with which these cabinets were originally *en suite*, was signed by Maggiolini.

French and Company, Inc., New York

Pierre-Paul Prud'hon

Cluny 1758—Paris 1823

Prud'hon studied at the Academy in Dijon under Devosge. From there he won the *Prix de Rome* in 1784. Though ten years younger than David, Prud'hon's more lyrical, introspective art associates him both with mid-eighteenth-century painting and with Romantic Neo-classicism, rather than with the heroics of David and his closest followers. Throughout the period of David's ascendancy, Prud'hon managed to maintain his personal style. He was patronized first by Josephine and later by the Empress Marie-Louise, as well as by Vivant Denon, Napoleon's Minister of Art.

107 *Justice and Divine Vengeance Pursuing Crime*, Study

Oil on canvas, 12-3/4 x 16-1/8 inches. Executed ca.1808.
Literature: John Maxon, "The Museum Revisited," RISD *Museum Notes*, II (Spring 1954).
A sketch for the picture now in the Louvre, which was exhibited by Prud'hon at the Paris Salon of 1808.

Museum of Art, Rhode Island School of Design

108 *Head of Vengeance*

Black and white chalk and estompe, on blue laid paper, 20 x 15-1/2 inches. Executed ca.1808.
Collections: Charles de Boisfremont (Lugt 353); Mme. Power (née de Boisfremont), (Sale, April 15-16, 1864, no. 40); Henri Didier (Sale, Hotel Drouot, Paris, June 15-17, 1868, no. 151); Dromont (Sale, Hotel Drouot, Paris, December 6-9, 1871, no. 819); P. Charles Séchan; J. P. M. Diéterle (Sale, Hotel Drouot, Paris, February 24-25, 1890, no. 36); Leon Ferté (Sale, Hotel Drouot, Paris, June 27, 1949, no. 16).

Exhibited: Paris, Ecole des Beaux-Arts, Exposition des oeuvres de Prud'hon, 1874, no. 226; Paris, Ecole des Beaux-Arts, Exposition P.-P. Prud'hon, 1922, no. 106.
Literature: Edmond de Goncourt, *Catalogue raisonné de l'oeuvre de P. P. Prud'hon* (Paris, 1876), pp. 166-167, no. 77. Clément-Janin, "Prud'hon: Ses gravures et ses graveurs," *La Renaissance de l'Art Français*, May 1922, p. 326. Jean Guiffrey, *L'Oeuvre de P.-P. Prud'hon* (Paris, 1924), no. 371.
A study for the painting *Justice and Divine Vengeance Pursuing Crime,* which was exhibited at the Paris Salon of 1808 and is now in the Louvre.

The Art Institute of Chicago, The Arthur Heun Fund

109 *The Union of Love and Friendship*

Oil on canvas, 57-1/2 x 44-1/2 inches. Executed ca.1793.
Collections: Saint-Marc Didot; Mme. Abel Vautier (inherited from her first husband, Saint-Marc Didot); Duc de Morny (Sale, May 31, June 1-3, 1865, no. 109); Baron Sellière (bought by him at the Morny sale); Albert de Rothschild; Baron Louis de Rothschild, Vienna.
Exhibited: Paris, Salon, 1793, no. 679 (supplement to catalogue); Paris, Musée Jacquemart-André, Prud'hon, 1958, no. 2; Dijon, Musée des Beaux-Arts, Prud'hon, 1959, no. 18 .
Literature: Charles Blanc, *Histoire des peintures de toutes les écoles, Ecole français,* III (Paris, 1863), 22. Edmond de Goncourt, *Catalogue raisonné de l'oeuvre de P. P. Prud'hon* (Paris, 1876), pp. 134-135, no. 56. Pierre Gauthiez, *Prud'hon* (Paris, 1886), p. 58. Edmond and Jules de Goncourt, *L'Art du XVIIIème siècle,* III (Paris, 1914), 383, 443. Jean Guiffrey, *L'Oeuvre de P.-P. Prud'hon* (Paris, 1924), pp. 14-16. Etienne Bricon, *Prud'hon* (Paris, n.d.), pp. 55-56.

Sometimes titled *Cupid and Psyche*. A drawing for it is in the Musée Condé, Chantilly.

Wildenstein & Co., Inc., New York

110 *Study of a Nude Woman, Seated, Looking to the Right* (VERSO: *Study of a Male Nude*)

Black and white chalk drawing, on blue paper, 24-3/8 x 17-1/4 inches.
Collections: Charles B. de Boisfremont, Paris (Lugt 353); Walter S. M. Burns, London (Sale, Sotheby & Co., London, May 6, 1926, no. 134).
Literature: Louise S. Richards, "Pierre Paul Prud'hon, Study of a Nude Woman," CMA *Bulletin,* L (February 1963), 25-28.

The Cleveland Museum of Art
Purchase from the J. H. Wade Fund

Jean Pierre Saint-Ours

Geneva 1752—Geneva 1809

Saint-Ours began his studies at the Academy in Paris in 1771, and was there a fellow pupil of David. He won first prizes for painting in 1778 and 1780. Using the money obtained for these pictures, Saint-Ours lived in Rome until 1792. Since he was a Protestant, he was not eligible to receive a royal pension. He then returned to Geneva. In 1803 he was made a member of the Institut de France.

111 *The Triumph of Beauty*

Oil on canvas, 30-3/4 x 53-3/8 inches.
Collection: Docteur Hippolyte Gosse, Geneva.

Musée d'art et d'histoire, Genève

Jacques Louis David

Paris 1748—Brussels 1825

A distant relative, Boucher, recommended that the young David be placed as a student with Vien in 1765. In 1774 David won the *Prix de Rome* with a picture which retained strong Rococo characteristics. In 1775 he went to Rome with Vien and remained there until 1781. It was at this time that David's style became truly Neo-classic. To the innovations which Hamilton had made, he added Cara-vaggesque lighting effects. In 1782 David was made a member of the Academy. He returned to Rome in 1784, where he painted *The Oath of the Horatii*, which announced his mature style. David supported the Revolution, became a deputy, and dictator of the arts. In 1798, the year David began the *Rape of the Sabines*, which demonstrated a new linearism of style, he met Napoleon and became an ardent Bonapartist. For Napoleon he painted great propaganda machines which depicted the important events of his regime. After Waterloo and the Bourbon restoration, David fled to Switzerland and later settled in Brussels, where he died.

112

112 Album Number Three

Various media, including pencil, Chinese ink, pen and bistre, on paper; drawings mounted in a folio 20 x 12-5/8 inches. Each drawing stamped with monograms of David's sons, affixed before the sale of 1826 (Lugt 839, 1437). Most of the drawings were executed during David's first Roman period, ca.1775–1780; a few were made later.

Collections: Jacques Louis David, (Sale, Paris, April 17, 1826, included in no. 66); David, (Sale, Paris, 1835); Baron Jeanin, 1835 (David's son-in-law); Marquise de Ludre (David's great-granddaughter).

Literature: Jules David, *Le Peintre Louis David,* I (Paris, 1880), 651, 653. Richard Cantinelli, *Jacques-Louis David* (Paris, 1930), p. 120. Klaus Holma, *David, son évolution et son style* (Paris, 1940), p. 113. Louis Hautecoeur, *Louis David* (Paris, 1954), p. 38.

Jacques Seligmann & Co., New York

113 Sketchbook

Pencil, pen, on paper, 8-1/2 x 5-1/2 inches. Executed 1775–1780 (dated erroneously and by a later hand 1788). *Collection:* Stated by Dowd, p. 195, to have been part of lot no. 66 of the David sale of 1826, but nowhere in this sketchbook are the collectors' marks applied before that sale visible.

Exhibited: Paris, Orangerie des Tuileries, David, 1948, no. 90 (dated here 1783).

Literature: W. R. Valentiner, *Jacques Louis David and the French Revolution* (New York, 1929), p. 8, figs. 7, 8, 10. Ernst Scheyer, "French Drawings of the Great Revolution and the Napoleonic Era," *Art Quarterly, IV* (Summer 1941), 187-204, figs. 3-4. David Lloyd Dowd, *Pageant-Master of the Republic* (Lincoln, Nebraska, 1948), p. 195, pl. IV.

W. R. Valentiner Estate

113

113

114 *The Oath of the Horatii*

Oil on canvas, 50 x 65 inches. Signed and dated (lower left): J. L. David faciebat,/Parisiis anno MDCCLXXXVI.

Collections: Painted for the Count de Vaudreuil (1740–1817) in 1786 (Sale, Paris, November 26, 1787, no. 107, to Lebrun); Firmin-Didot family, by 1794 to after 1880; Hyacinthe Didot, 1880; Louis Delamarre, Paris, by 1913; Baronne Eugène d'Huart.

Exhibited: Paris, Galerie Lebrun (au profit des Grecs), 1826, no. 40; Paris, Petit Palais, David et ses élèves, 1913, no. 25.

Literature: Jacques Louis David, Autograph list of his paintings, ca.1815 (mentions "les horaces, repetition en petit"). Thierry, *Guide des Amateurs et Etrangers*, II (Paris, 1787), 148. Anonymous, *Notice sur la vie et les ouvrages de M. Jacques-Louis David* (Paris, 1824), p. 43. Antoine Thomé de Gamond, *Vie de David, Premier Peintre de Napoleon* (Brussels, 1826), p. 162. P.-A. Coupin,

"Notice Nécrologique sur Jacques-Louis David," *Revue Encyclopedique*, XXXIV (April 1827), 53. Jules David, *Le Peintre Louis David, 1748–1825; Souvenirs et Documents inédits*, I (Paris, 1880–1882), 636. Richard Cantinelli, *Jacques-Louis David, 1748–1825* (Brussels and Paris, 1930), no. 48. Klaus Holma, *David, son évolution et son style* (Paris, 1940), pp. 48, 126, no. 54. Michel Florisoone, *David, Exposition en l'honneur du deuxième centenaire de sa naissance* (Paris, 1948), p. 48. John Canaday, *Mainstreams of Modern Art* (New York, 1959), pp. 11-12. Otto Whitman, "L'Art Française au Musée de Toledo," *Connaissance des Arts*, no. 125 (July 1962), 40-47. Alan Gowans, *Images of American Living. . . .* (New York and Philadelphia, 1964), pp. 252-253, no. 88c.

Engraved by A. A. Morel, 1810. A smaller version, with variations, of the picture which David painted in Rome in 1784 and which is now in the Louvre.

The Toledo Museum of Art
Gift of Edward Drummond Libbey

115 *The Lictors Bring Back to Brutus the Bodies of His Sons*

Oil on canvas, 27-13/16 x 35-3/4 inches. Signed and dated (lower left): J. L. David f.ᵇᵃᵗ parisiis/anno 1789.
Collection: Anonymous sale, Paris, December 12, 1925.
Literature: "A Painting by David," *Bulletin of Wadsworth Atheneum,* XII (October-December 1934), 36-38. Klaus Holma, *David, son évolution et son style* (Paris, 1940), no. 70. David Lloyd Dowd, *Pageant-Master of the Republic* (Lincoln, Nebraska, 1948), pl. VI. Michel Florisoone, *David, Exposition en l'honneur du deuxième centenaire de sa naissance* (Paris, 1948), p. 56.
A small version of David's painting in the Louvre. A sketch exists in the Museum in Stockholm, and other copies or versions are known. The painting in the Louvre was first exhibited at the Salon of 1789, just after the start of the Revolution. The subject, which demonstrates the virtue of a Roman under the Republic, was felt by many contemporaries to be in sharp contrast with the behavior of their own king. It was largely by virtue of the subject chosen for this picture that David became associated with the Revolution.

Wadsworth Atheneum, Hartford
The Ella Gallup Sumner and Mary Catlin Sumner
Collection

116 *Cupid and Psyche*

Oil on canvas, 72-1/2 x 95-1/8 inches. Signed and dated (on couch): L. DAVID 1817 BRUXELLES.

Collections: Comte Sommariva (1817–Sale, Paris, February 18–23, 1839 [1842?], no. 1, to Dubois); Comte Pourtales (Sale, Paris, March 27, 1865, no. 242, to Mme. de Furtado); Mme. de Furtado (1880); Prince Murat (1913); Princess Murat (Sale, Palais Galliera, Paris, March 2, 1961, no. 140, pl. 1).

Exhibited: Brussels, Musée Royal, Jacques Louis David, 1817; Paris, Galerie Lebrun (au profit des Grecs), 1826; Paris, Petit Palais, David et ses élèves, 1913, no. 60; Paris, Orangerie des Tuileries, David, 1948, pp. 28, 100, no. 72.

Literature: Edme François Antoine Marie Miel, *Essai sur les Beaux-Arts et le Salon de 1817*, pp. 238–239, pl. 29. Antoine Thomé de Gamond, *Vie de Louis David* (Paris, 1826), pp. 209–210, 237. E. J. Delecluze, *Louis David, son école et son temps: souvenirs* (Paris, 1855), pp. 367 ff.

Paul Mantz, "La Galerie Pourtales," *Gazette des Beaux-Arts*, XVIII (1865), 113-114. Jules David, *Le Peintre Louis David, Souvenirs et Documents Inédits* (Paris, 1880), pp. 540–544, 546, 580–581, 649. Robert Rey, "Le Moins Davidien des Davidiens," *L'Art Vivant* (December 15, 1925), p. 10. Richard Cantinelli, *David* (Paris, 1930), no. 143. Klaus Holma, *David, son évolution et son style* (Paris, 1940), pp. 94–95. André Maurois, *Les Demi-Dieux. J. L. David* (Paris, 1948), pp. 36-37. Douglas Cooper, "Jacques Louis David: a Bi-Centenary Exhibition," *The Burlington Magazine*, XC (October, 1948), 279. Louis Hautecoeur, *Louis David* (Paris, 1954), pp. 242, 267, 268 ff., 273, 306. Jack Lindsay, *Death of a Hero* (London, 1960), pp. 144–145. Henry S. Francis, "Jacques Louis David: Cupid and Psyche," CMA *Bulletin*, L (February 1963), 29–34.

Engraved by Potrelle, Giboy, and Jules David.

The Cleveland Museum of Art
Purchase, Leonard C. Hanna Jr. Bequest

Montpellier 1766—Montpellier 1837

Fabre was a pupil first of Vien, then of David. In 1787 he won the *Prix de Rome*. He then went to Italy, where he remained until 1826, working chiefly in Florence. Fabre painted many portraits, as well as the history pictures which he exhibited regularly at the Salon. He was also a collector of art, and gave to his native city the collection which became the nucleus of the museum there which bears his name.

117 *Virgil Reads the Aeneid to the Family of Augustus*

Oil on canvas, 43-7/8 x 56-1/4 inches.
Literature: AIC *Quarterly*, LVII (Winter 1963–1964), illustrated, p. 2.

The Art Institute of Chicago, Wirt D. Walker Fund

Henry Fuseli
(Johann Heinrich Füssli)

Zürich 1741—London 1825

Though his father, brothers, and sisters were artists, the young Fuseli was ordained a clergyman in 1761. Two years later, because of a political attack which he had made, Fuseli was forced to leave Zürich. He chose to go to Berlin. There he pursued a career more literary than artistic, and met the British ambassador who offered to take him to England. Fuseli arrived in London in 1764. It was there that he decided to follow an artistic, rather than a literary career. In 1770 he went to Rome, where he was to remain for eight years. During this time Fuseli developed his personal style, basing it largely upon what he learned from studying Michelangelo. Fairly soon after his return to London he established a reputation for himself as a history painter. He became a member of the Royal Academy in 1790, and in 1800 was made its professor of painting.

118 *Mother and Child:*
A Mythological Subject

Oil on canvas, 38-7/8 x 50 inches. Painted ca.1790 (?).
Yale University Art Gallery
Gift of Yale University Art Gallery Associates

119 *Hercules and Diomedes*

Black crayon, pen and wash, 19-3/4 x 15-1/8 inches. Executed before 1807.
Literature: Paul Ganz, *Die Zeichnungen Hans Heinrich Füsslis* (Bern, 1947), p. 69, no. 67.
Engraved by Heinrich Lips for the *Sämtliche Werke Heinrich Füsslis nebst einem Versuche Seiner Biographie* (Zürich, 1807), p. 74.

The Art Institute of Chicago
The Leonora Hall Gurley Memorial Collection

120 *The Artist Moved by the Grandeur of Antique Ruins*

Red chalk washed, 16-3/8 x 14 inches. Inscribed by unknown hand (lower right): 8(5?) W. Blake. Executed ca.1778–1780.
Collections: Baroness North; Paul Hürlimann, Zürich.
Exhibited: Kunsthaus Zürich, Johann Heinrich Füssli, 1941, no. 251. Rome, Palazzo delle Esposizioni, Il Settecento a Roma, 1959, p. 109, no. 226.
Probably executed in Zürich between October 1778 and April 1779.

Kunsthaus Zürich

John Flaxman

York 1755—London 1826

Flaxman grew up in London, where his father was a molder and seller of plaster casts. He was encouraged at an early age by Romney, who was a customer of his father. He also became a friend of Blake. In the early 1770's he exhibited regularly at the Academy. He needed money, however, so he went to work for Wedgwood and Bentley, making models to be reproduced in ceramics. He worked for them from 1775 to 1787. During this time he also did some mortuary sculpture. In 1787 Flaxman went to Italy, where he made the drawings for the *Iliad* and the *Odyssey* illustrations. After his return from Italy, Flaxman enjoyed a quiet but continuous success for the remainder of his life.

121 *Ulysses at the Table of Circe*

Pen, ink, and wash over light pencil, on paper, 8-1/8 x 10-1/2 inches. Inscribed (bottom center): Untouched before thee stand the cates divine,/and unregarded laughs the rosy wine./Odyssey; Book 10, line 447. Executed ca.1790.

One of the drawings illustrating the *Odyssey*, commissioned by Mrs. Hare Naylor and later engraved by Piroli.

John Herron Museum of Art, Indianapolis

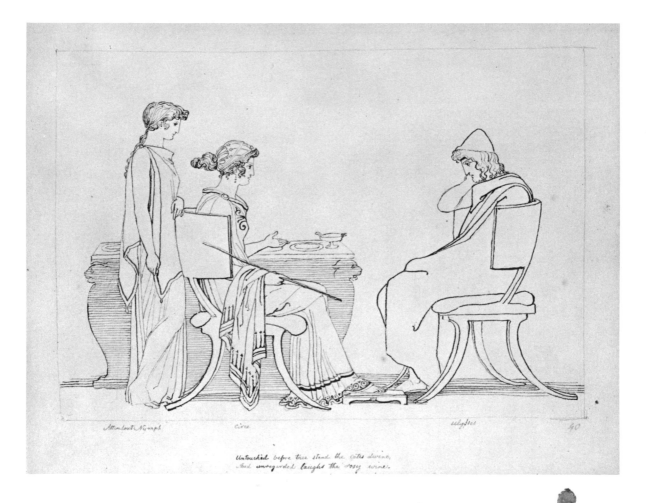

Untouched before thee stand the cates divine,
And unregarded laughs the rosy wine.

William Blake

London 1757—London 1827

Blake was born into the family of a shopkeeper. His talent as a draughtsman was early recognized and he was sent at fifteen to a drawing school kept by Henry Pars. In 1777 he was apprenticed to an engraver, and the next year he entered the school of the Royal Academy. Blake received little recognition in his lifetime. He supported himself by keeping a shop and engraving other men's work. Most of the illustrated books upon which his fame rests were published by himself. The mystical subject matter of Blake's work is far removed from the usual content of Neo-classicism, but his style has close affinities with several Neo-classic artists, especially Fuseli.

122 *The Holy Family*
(*Christ in the Lap of Truth*)

Water-color drawing, 14-15/16 x 12-13/16 inches. Signed (lower left): inv./WB.
Collections: T. Butts; H. G. John; A. A. Weston; Graham Robertson; Sale, Christie's, London, July 22, 1949, no. 24.
Exhibited: London, International Exhibition, 1862, no. 221; London, Burlington Fine Arts Club, 1876, no. 144.
Literature: Helene Richter, *William Blake* (Strassburg, 1906), pl. V. Basil De Sélincourt, *William Blake* (London and New York, 1909), p. 201. Archibald G. B. Russell, "The Graham Robertson Collection," *The Burlington Magazine,* XXXVII (July 1920), 34. Geoffrey Keynes, ed., *The Note-Book of William Blake, called the Rossetti Manuscript* (London, 1935), no. 207.

The Cleveland Museum of Art, John L. Severance Fund

Johan Tobias Sergel

Stockholm 1740—Stockholm 1814

In 1757 Sergel became the pupil of a French sculptor working in Stockholm, Larchevêque. He went with Larchevêque to Paris in 1758 and studied there at the Royal Academy. He returned to Stockholm and soon obtained commissions from the king and won a gold medal at the Academy in Stockholm in 1760. In 1767 he went to Rome with a stipend from the Crown. The following year he visited Naples, Pompeii, and Herculaneum. In Rome he worked for a time at the French Academy. In 1778 Sergel was appointed court sculptor to Gustavus III, and returned to Sweden the next year, after a sojourn in Paris. The remainder of his life was devoted to executing many commissions for the king and for other Swedish patrons.

123 Design for a Fountain

Pen, brown and grey wash over red chalk, 22 x 16-1/2 inches. Executed ca.1770.

Nationalmuseum, Stockholm

124 *The Faun*

Marble, 17-3/4 inches high. Signed and dated (back edge of base) : I. T. SERGELL, ROMAE./MDCCLXXIV.
Collection: King Gustavus III.
Literature: George Göthe, *Johan Tobias Sergels Skulpturverk* (Stockholm, 1921), pp. 12-13, 47, no. 20. Oscar Antonsson, *Sergels ungdom och romtid* (Stockholm, 1942), pp. 160-166. Ragnar Josephson, *Sergels fantasi* (Stockholm, 1956), pp. 157-166.
Preceded by several preparatory pen drawings and two terra cottas, one smaller than the final version and made in Rome about 1769, the other of approximately the same size and inscribed "I. Sergell. fecit. Romae. 1770." Both terra cottas are in the Nationalmuseum, Stockholm. A replica in marble belongs to the Ateneum Museum, Helsingfors, Finland.

Nationalmuseum, Stockholm

124

123

126

125

125 *Diomedes, Odysseus, and a Dead Warrior*

Pen, 10-1/2 x 7-9/16 inches. Executed ca.1771.
Literature: George Göthe, *Johan Tobias Sergel* (Stockholm, 1898), p. 65. Harald Brising, *Sergels konst* (Stockholm, 1914), p. 76, fig. 65. Oscar Antonsson, *Sergels ungdom och romtid* (Stockholm, 1942), p. 177. Ragnar Josephson, *Sergels fantasi*, I (Stockholm, 1956), 176, fig. 243.

Nationalmuseum, Stockholm

126 *Venus and Anchises Embracing*

Pen, brown and grey wash, 8-1/4 x 6 inches. Executed ca.1769.
Literature: Oscar Antonsson, *Sergels ungdom och romtid* (Stockholm, 1942), p. 212.

Nationalmuseum, Stockholm

Pierre-Narcisse Guérin

Paris 1774—Rome 1833

Though never a pupil of David, Guérin, almost inevitably, was strongly influenced by him. He won the *Prix de Rome* in 1797, but he did not go there because of the suspension of the school during Napoleon's Italian campaign. In 1799 he won a success at the Salon with his picture, *Return of Marius Sextus*. Guérin, though not insensitive in the handling of line, was inclined toward rather sentimental subjects. He was made director of the Academy in Rome and was a very successful teacher.

128 *Aeneas and Dido*

Oil on canvas, 13-3/4 x 17-3/4 inches. Painted ca.1815.
Collection: Adrien Aimé Destouches.
Exhibited: Paris, Petit Palais, Gros, ses amis, ses élèves, 1936, no. 333; Paris, Atelier de Delacroix, Delacroix et ses compagnons de jeunesse, 1947, no. 35; London, Tate Gallery, The Romantic Movement, 1959, no. 203,
Literature: Edme François Antoine Marie Miel, *Essai sur les Beaux-Arts et le Salon de 1817.* Gaston Brière, *Louvre, Catalogue des peintures, Ecole français,* I (Paris, 1924), no. 397A. Raymond Escholier, *La peinture française au XIXème siècle: De David à Géricault* (Paris, 1941), p. 104. Charles Sterling and Hélène Adhemar, *Musée du Louvre, Peintures du XIXème siècle,* II (Paris, 1959), no. 1011, pl. 364.
A sketch for the painting by Guérin exhibited in the Salon of 1817, now also in the Louvre, which is signed and dated 1815. There is a reduction of the composition at the Musée de Bordeaux. Many other versions of this sketch exist.

Musée du Louvre

127 *The Vigil*

Lithograph, 10-11/16 x 7-3/4 inches. Inscribed: (left), R. E./P. G.; (below), Le Vigilant. Executed 1816.
Exhibited: The Cleveland Museum of Art, The Art of Lithography, 1948–1949, no. 222, pl. VII.
Literature: Henri Béraldi, *Les graveurs du XIX siècle,* VIII (Paris, 1889), 6.

The Cleveland Museum of Art
Mr. and Mrs. Lewis B. Williams Collection

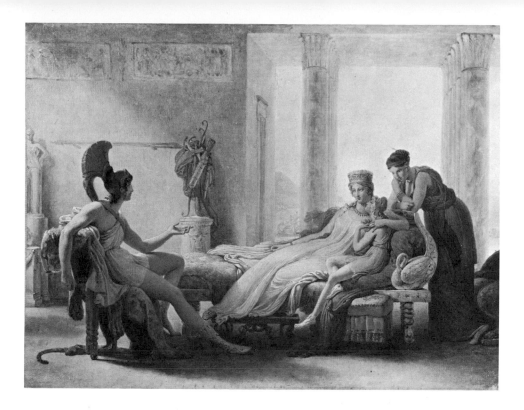

Anne Louis Girodet de Roucy called de Trioson

Montargis 1767—Paris 1834

In 1785 Girodet became a pupil of David, and won the *Prix de Rome* in 1789. He was at the Academy in Rome when, in 1793, David's order to replace the Royal arms with those of the Republic touched off a riot in which a mob wrecked the Academy. In that same year Girodet sent from Italy to Paris his *Endymion*, which announced his independence from David and a move toward Romantic Neo-classicism. David disapproved of his new stance. In 1812 Girodet inherited a large fortune and abandoned painting.

129 *Seated Nude in a Twilight Landscape*

Oil on canvas, 63 x 45 inches. Signed (on tree at right): Girodet fecit.

Ponce Museum of Art, Puerto Rico
Luis A. Ferré Foundation

Jean Auguste Dominique Ingres

Montauban 1780—Paris 1867

Ingres' father, himself an artist, recognized his son's talent at an early age and sent him first to the Academy at Toulouse in 1791 and then to Paris to study with David in 1797. By that date the movement away from David's mature style was well under way and Ingres, influenced by Flaxman, was quick to join it. He won the *Prix de Rome* in 1801, but did not actually go to Rome until 1806. Once in Italy, he stayed for eighteen years, surviving chiefly by making portrait drawings of foreign visitors. In 1824 his *Vow of Louis XIII* was exhibited at the Salon with enormous success. He returned to Paris and for the remainder of his life led the Classicists who stood in opposition to Delacroix and the rising tide of Romanticism.

130 *Sappho*

Water color, 8-1/2 x 11-1/2 inches. Painted probably before 1810.
Literature: Douglas Cooper, *Great Private Collections* (New York, 1963), p. 149.
Though traditionally known as *Sappho*, the subject of this water color may be drawn from Madame de Staël's *Corinne in Italy*, first published in 1807.

Forsyth Wickes, Newport, Rhode Island

131 *Oedipus and the Sphinx*

Oil on canvas, 42-1/2 x 34-1/4 inches. Signed and dated (center foreground): J. Ingres P.bat/etatis/LXXXIII/1864. *Collections:* Painted for M. Emile Pereire; Messrs. Pereire (Sale, Paris, 1872, no. 26); E. Secrétan (Sale, Paris, 1889, no. 37); Chéramy (Sale, Paris, 1908, no. 208); Henry Walters Collection.
Exhibited: New York, Paul Rosenberg & Co., Ingres in American Collections, 1961, no. 72.

Literature: Henri Delaborde, *Ingres, sa vie, ses travaux, sa doctrine* . . . (Paris, 1870), p. 212, no. 36. Edward S. King, "Ingres as Classicist," WAG *Journal*, V (1942), 69 ff., fig. 1, note 14. Georges Wildenstein, *Ingres* (London, 1954), pp. 173, 231, no. 315, fig. 32. Norman Schlenoff, *Ingres, ses sources littéraires* (Paris, 1956), pl. XIII.
A version, in reverse, of a painting in the Louvre. Though dated 1864, the Walters version was probably begun about 1835.

The Walters Art Gallery, Baltimore

132 *Seated Female Nude*

Graphite pencil, on white paper, 12-7/16 x 8 inches. Signed (lower right): Ingres. Stamp of Ingres sale, lower left. Executed 1841–1867.
Collections: Ingres Sale; Miss Etta Cone, Baltimore, after 1934.
Exhibited: New York, Paul Rosenberg and Co., Ingres in American Collections, 1961, no. 53.

The Baltimore Museum of Art, Cone Collection

133 *Pompeian Motifs*

Attributed to Ingres

Pencil and water color on faded buff paper and pen and brush, 10-11/16 x 20-7/8 inches. Executed ca.1810–1820.
Literature: Agnes Mongan, "Three Drawings by Ingres," *Art Quarterly*, XVIII (Summer 1955), 180-185, fig. 2.
A design for a wall decoration in the antique style.

Fogg Art Museum, Harvard University
William C. Heilman Fund
and Paul J. Sachs 70th Anniversary Exhibition Fund

Antoine-Denis Chaudet

Paris 1763—Paris 1810

Chaudet was a sculptor, painter, and draughtsman. He was a pupil of Stouf and Gois. In 1784 he won the *Prix de Rome* and went to Italy. By 1789 he was back in Paris and was made a member of the Academy. Under Napoleon, Chaudet executed many commissions for architectural decorations and for portraits, including several of the emperor. Chaudet also made models to be reproduced at the Sèvres porcelain factory.

134 *Bust of Napoleon I*

Marble, 24-1/2 inches high. Signed (right side): chaudet, f. Inscribed (rear): G.B.C. Executed ca.1808.

The Emperor wears a laurel wreath on his head and around his shoulders a narrow band resembling the Roman *angustus clavus*, which signified equestrian rank.

The Phoenix Art Museum

François Rude

Dijon 1784—Paris 1855

Rude studied first with Devosge in Dijon. In 1805 he went to Paris where he was a pupil of Edme Gaulle and Cartellier. In 1812 he won the *Prix de Rome*. He remained there two years and then returned to Dijon. By 1823 he was in Brussels, where he did various architectural decorations. In 1827 he was back in Paris, which was the center of his activities for the remainder of his life. Only Rude's early works are Neo-classic in style. Later he was among the first to apply the Romantic style to sculpture.

135 *Aristaeus Lamenting the Loss of His Bees*

Bronze, 35-1/2 inches high. Signed and dated 1803.
Collections: Cambacérès, acquired by the Museum in Dijon in 1955.
Exhibited: Musée des Beaux-Arts de Dijon, François Rude, Commémoration du Centenaire, 1955, no: 10, pl. IV.
Literature: Pierre Quarré, "François Rude, Grand Prix de Rome," *Mémoires de l'Académie de Dijon,* CXII (1958), fig. 1. Musée des Beaux-Arts de Dijon, *Catalogue de Sculptures* (Dijon, 1960), no. 732. Pierre Quarré, "François Rude à Bruxelles," *Industrie,* no. 10 (October 1962).
The subject corresponds to the theme of the concours of the Ecole des Beaux-Arts in 1812, in which Rude won the grand *Prix de Rome.* It was executed after the model in plaster which was broken by the artist in 1843.

Musée des Beaux-Arts de Dijon

136 *Achilles on His Chariot Drags the Body of Hector around the Walls of Troy*

Black crayon, 7-1/2 x 14-1/8 inches. Executed ca.1823.
Collection: Joliet, Dijon.
Exhibited: Musée des Beaux-Arts de Dijon, François Rude, Commémoration du Centenaire, 1955, no. 50 (7).
Literature: Louis de Fourcaud, *François Rude, sculpteur* . . . (Paris, 1904), p. 447. Paul Vitry, "Les dessins de Rude au Musée de Dijon," *Gazette des Beaux-Arts,* 6e periode, IV (August 1930), 113-127. Pierre Quarré, *Musée de Dijon, Quatorze dessins d'Artistes bourguignons* (Dijon, 1943), no. 13. Pierre Quarré, "François Rude à Bruxelles," *Industrie,* no. 10 (October 1962).
The first project for one of the eight bas-reliefs depicting the *Life of Achilles* which were made to decorate the Château de Tervueren near Brussels. The reliefs, executed in 1823–1824, were destroyed in a fire of 1879. Drawings for them are conserved at the Musée Rude at Dijon.

Musée des Beaux-Arts de Dijon

Guillaume Beneman

Master 1785—after 1811

A native of Germany, Beneman became an independent cabinetmaker just before the Revolution. Because of motives of economy, Reisener, who had been the favorite cabinetmaker to the Crown for most of the reign of Louis XVI, fell from popularity in 1785. Beneman, working under Hauré, took over his position, but little new furniture was made. Beneman continued working after the Revolution and in 1811 was put in charge of the Garde-Meuble Impérial.

137 Secretary

Mahogany with gilt bronze mounts and grey marble top, 56-1/4 inches high. Stamped (three times): G. Beneman. Executed ca.1800.
Collection: Reported to have come from the Court of Holland.
Literature: D. Graeme Keith, "Two Important Additions to the Furniture Collection," RISD *Museum Notes*, XLII (1956), 15-17.
A very similar secretary and commode, *en suite*, exist at Fountainebleau. Adolf Feulner, *Kunstgeschichte des Möbels* (Berlin, 1927), pp. 587-590, fig. 473, has published the pieces from Fontainebleau as having been made for Queen Hortense of Holland, and mentions that they are dependent upon designs by Percier and Fontaine. More recently, the Fontainebleau pieces have again been published, together with the designs by Percier and Fontaine upon which they were based, but without a note about their provenance. See [Jean Meuvret], *Les Ebénistes du XVIIIᵉ Siècle Français* (Paris, 1963), p. 314, figs. 1, 2, 3, 4.

Providence Art Club, on loan to the Museum of Art
Rhode Island School of Design

138 Secretary

Anonymous, France

Amboyna wood with gilt bronze mounts, 68-1/4 inches high. Executed ca.1810.

The Metropolitan Museum of Art, Rogers Fund, 1923

139 Tripod Table

Anonymous, France

Gilt bronze with marble top, 35-1/2 inches high. Executed ca.1800.

Probably copied from an ancient Roman bronze example found at Pompeii. See Vittorio Spinazzola, *Le Arti Decorative in Pompeii e nel Museo Nazionale di Napoli* (Milan, 1928), pl. 257.

Cincinnati Art Museum

Charles Percier

Paris 1764—Paris 1838

Percier was a pupil of the noted architect Peyre. Together with his partner, Fontaine, Percier became the leading architect of France under Napoleon. Since, however, little new construction was undertaken during that period, their practice was largely limited to redesigning the interiors of already existing buildings. The style which they developed, following the lead suggested by David before the Revolution, became widely influential throughout Europe by means of publications of their designs.

140 Design for Chairs

Pencil, 4-1/8 x 7-5/8 inches. Signed (lower left): Percier. Executed ca.1800.

The Metropolitan Museum of Art, Whittelsey Fund, 1953

Pierre Philippe Thomire

Paris 1751—Paris 1843

Thomire was the son of a sculptor and studied at the Academie de St.-Luc in Paris. He became a very skillful bronze caster, and was especially noted for the quality and finish of his gilded bronzes. Before the Revolution, he is recorded as having made gilt bronze mounts for furniture and porcelains. After the Revolution he specialized in objects made entirely of gilt bronze. He also made fine bronze copies of popular sculptures.

142 Pair of Candelabra

Gilt bronze, 50-1/4 inches high. Signed (on back of base): THOMIRE à PARIS. Executed ca.1815–1825.
Collection: Said to have been made by Thomire for Louis XVIII.
A pair of candelabra with somewhat different candle branches and a simpler base are shown in a painting by Dubois-Drahonet, engraved by Normand, of the Duchesse de Berri in 1827. See Henri Bouchot, *Le luxe français, La restauration;* . . . (Paris, 1893), p. 73.

The Metropolitan Museum of Art
Bequest of James Alexander Scrymser, 1926

141 Centerpiece: *Bacchus and Ariadne*

Attributed to Pierre Philippe Thomire
Gilt bronze and marble, 15 inches high. Executed ca.1790.
The Phoenix Art Museum

143 Candelabrum

Anonymous, France

Gilt bronze, 35-1/2 inches high. Executed ca.1810.
Collections: Said to come from the Château of Saint-Cloud; Hoentschel, Paris.
Literature: André Pérate and Gaston Brière, *Collection George Hoentschel*, IV (Paris, 1908), pl. LX. For designs by Percier for similar candelabra see Union centrale des arts décoratifs, *Recueil de dessins d'orfèvrerie du premier empire par Percier et Biennais . . .* (Paris, n.d.), pls. 13, 61.

The Metropolitan Museum of Art
Gift of J. Pierpont Morgan, 1906

Martin Guillaume Biennais

1764–1843

Biennais did not become an important, independent maker of silver until after the Revolution. With Odiot, he was the most famous silversmith during the Empire. He worked extensively for Napoleon. Biennais retired in 1819.

144 Tureen

After Designs by Percier and Fontaine

Silver gilt, 18-1/4 inches high. Borghese Arms engraved and applied. Executed 1794–1814.
Collections: From a service said to have been given by Napoleon to his sister Pauline and her husband, Prince Camillo Borghese; Princess Borghese, Rome (ca.1803?–1892); Prince Paolo Borghese (Sale, Palazzo Borghese, Rome, March 28-April 9, 1892, no. 847, pl. XI); Don Antonio Licata, Prince of Baucina (1892–); Mrs. Edith Rockefeller McCormick, by 1924 (Sale, American Art Association, New York, January 2-6, 1934, no. 701).
Literature: L'union centrale des arts décoratifs, *Receuil de dessins d'orfèvrerie du premier empire par Percier et Biennais . . .* (Paris, n.d.), pl. 10. Henry Nocq, P. Alfassa, and J. Guérin, *Orfèvrerie civile française*, II (Paris, n.d.), pl. LXVIII. C. Louise Avery, "French Empire Silver," MMA *Bulletin*, XXIX (April 1934), 64-66. Faith Dennis, *Three Centuries of French Domestic Silver* (New York, 1960), p. 76, no. 63.

The Metropolitan Museum of Art
Purchase, 1934, Joseph Pulitzer Bequest

Jean-Baptiste Claude Odiot

1763–1850

With Biennais, Odiot was the most important French silversmith under the Empire. He also worked extensively for Napoleon, and he sometimes cooperated with Biennais, as for example in the creation of the Borghese service.

145 Jewel Box

Silver gilt, 9-5/8 inches long. Executed ca.1820.

The Museum of Fine Arts, Boston
Gift of Miss Salome H. Snow

146 Plate: *Head of a Woman*

Anonymous, Sèvres Factory, France

Porcelain, 9-1/8 inches in diameter. Signed (recto): Moriot. Marked: (verso, in red), M. Imp^{Le}/de Sevres/8; (verso, in blue), A.M. Executed 1808.

The mark "A.M." was employed by François-Adolphe Moriot, one of several painters of that name employed at the Sèvres factory. He is not recorded as having worked there as early as 1808.

The Minneapolis Institute of Arts
Bequest of Alfred Duane Pell

147 Plate: *Antinous*

Anonymous, Sèvres Factory, France

Porcelain, 9-3/8 inches in diameter. Marked (verso, in red): De Sevres/10. Signed (verso): Mlle. de Gaulle. Executed 1810.

A painter of figures whose name, Jean-Marie Degault, was signed in full, was active at Sèvres from 1808 to 1817. The style of painting of the present plate resembles that of published works by Degault.

The Minneapolis Institute of Arts
Bequest of Alfred Duane Pell

148 Lyre-Guitar

M. C. Mousset, France

Wood, 30-3/4 inches long. Inscribed (within sound box):
M. C. Mousset. Executed ca.1800–1825.
In 1806 this sort of instrument was described thus: "The
new Lyre (Guitar), which only a few years ago appeared
in France, the ordinary Guitar being made to imitate the
ancient Lyre, is a welcome sight to lovers of the beautiful
forms of antiquity." The instrument was only made until
about 1825. The name of the maker of the present example
does not appear to have been previously recorded.

The Cleveland Museum of Art
Gift of Ralph King in memory of Charles G. King, Jr.

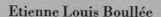
Etienne Louis Boullée

Paris 1728—Paris 1799

Boullée was the pupil first of the painter Pierre, then
of Lejay. He was one of the pioneers in the introduction of the Neo-classic style in architecture. Although
a number of buildings were constructed to his designs, few have survived. Late in life he published a
series of architectural designs which rival those of
Ledoux in their representation of a tendency of Neo-
classic architecture toward geometric purity of form.

149 Design for a Museum

Attributed to Boullée

Pencil, pen and ink with water color, on paper, 8-1/4 x
16-5/8 inches. Inscribed (on frieze of building): TEMPLE
DE LA CURIOSITÉ. Executed ca.1790.
Collection: Léon Decloux, Sèvres, until 1911.
Literature: Richard P. Wunder, "The Architect's Eye,"
CUM *Chronicle,* III (September 1956), 31, no. 87.

The Cooper Union Museum, New York

Antonio Canova

Possagno 1757—Venice 1822

Canova grew up in the house of his grandfather, a stonemason. His early efforts at sculpture attracted attention, and he was apprenticed to Giuseppe Torretti. In 1769 he followed his master to Venice. Canova's *Daedalus and Icarus* of 1779 was widely noticed in Venice and he was given a scholarship to go to Rome. Shortly after his arrival there, he met Gavin Hamilton. As a result of Hamilton's influence, Canova adapted the early Neo-classic style to sculpture. He soon earned a considerable reputation in Rome, and by the time he died, Canova was generally considered the greatest contemporary sculptor in Europe.

150 *Four Dancing Figures*

Oil on canvas, 27 x 45 inches. Painted ca.1793.
Collection: British private collection.
A *modello* for four figures in Canova's tempera decorations in the Casa Canova, Possagno. See Elena Bassi, *La Gipsoteca di Possagno* (Venice, 1957), nos. 124, 122, 120, 119. The composition of one figure was used in 1811 in the statue *Danzatrice Col Ditto al Mano* (Rome, Galleria Corsini). Other drawings and monochromes related in style and subject to the present work are at Bassano. See Bassi, *Il Museo Civico di Bassano, I Disegni di Antonio Canova* (Venice, 1959).

Anthony M. Clark, Minneapolis

151 *Lady Reclining in a Chair*

Ink on white paper, 6-1/4 x 7-5/8 inches. Inscribed: (verso, lower right), Nro: 42; (verso, lower left), 19. Stamped (verso, lower left): Sphinx with one paw encircling a shield.

Fogg Art Museum, Harvard University
Meta and Paul J. Sachs Collection

152 *Kreugas*

Bronze with black patina, 25-1/2 inches high. Inscribed (on base): fecit Antonio Canova Roma 1806.
Collection: Prince Trivulzio, Milan.
Literature: Phillip Fehl, "A Statuette of the Pugilist Creugas by Antonio Canova," MAUK *Register*, I (June 1958), 13-24.
A reduction of a marble by Canova, completed in 1802, now in the Vatican Museum. The subject is derived from a passage in Pausanias' *Description of Greece* in which he describes a fight between Kreugas and Damoxenos, the latter the subject of a sculpture now also in the Vatican. Canova's Kreugas was dependent in composition upon the incorrectly restored Roman copy after Kritio's *Harmodious*, now in Naples. The position assumed by Kreugas is explained by the story to be illustrated. He and Damoxenos had agreed to exchange undefended blows. Kreugas had done so. Damoxenos is about to deliver the blow which both men know will kill Kreugas.

The University of Kansas Museum of Art
Gift of the Endowment Association

Andrea Appiani

Milan 1754—Milan 1817

Appiani is one of the best-known of Italian Neo-classic artists, and the leading painter of his day in Lombardy. He was the pupil of Carlo Maria Giudici and was influenced by the Florentine painter Traballesi. Appiani was a skillful painter in both oil and fresco. He was also an accomplished portraitist. Napoleon recognized his talents, made him his official painter in Italy and granted him the Legion d'Honneur.

153 *Toilet of Juno*

Pencil and white chalk, on brown paper, 11-3/4 x 17 inches.
Collection: Roman private collection, late nineteenth century.
For a related drawing see C. Maltese, "L'éta neoclassica in Lombardia," *Bollettino d'Arte,* XLIV (July-September, 1959), 285-289, fig. 3.

Mr. and Mrs. Milton J. Lewine, New York

Felice Giani

San Sebastiano near Genoa 1758—Rome 1823

Giani was a pupil first of Bianchi and Antonio Galli Bibiena in Pavia, then (about 1778) of Pedrini and Gandolfi in Bologna, and finally from 1780 of Batoni, Unterberger, and Antolini at the Accademia di San Luca in Rome. Giani executed painted decorations for rooms and did illustrations. After 1800 he went to Paris where he did decorations for Napoleon at the Tuileries. He returned to Italy and executed decorations in many North Italian cities. It is Giani's fertility of invention and his power as a draughtsman which have recently caused his work to be re-examined with some interest.

154 *An Academic Investiture*

Pen and colored washes, on paper, 18-1/4 x 23 inches. Executed ca.1794.
Probably executed in Naples.

John Maxon, Chicago

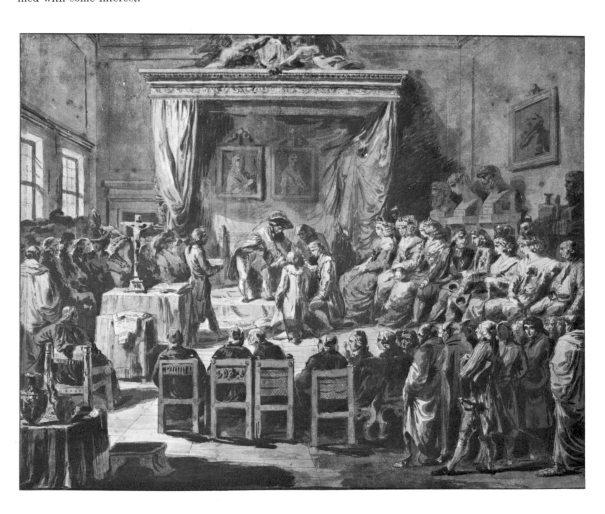

155 *Hector Attacking the Ships of the Greeks*

Ink and wash over light pencil, on white paper, 19-1/2 x 14 inches.
Collection: Roman private collection, late nineteenth century.

Mr. and Mrs. Milton J. Lewine, New York

156 *The Vestal Virgins Showing the Will of Augustus to Tiberius and the Senate*

Pen, brown ink, and wash, heightened with white, over black chalk, 19-3/8 x 34-3/4 inches.
Collections: Piancastelli; Mary Brandegee (Lugt 1860c); Janos Scholz.
Literature: RISD *Museum Notes*, XLIV (March 1958), 10, fig. 8.

Museum of Art, Rhode Island School of Design

157 Designs for Ceiling Decorations

A. *Aurora.* Pencil, pen and ink with water colors, on paper, 13-1/16 x 11-13/16 inches.
B. *Iris and the Rainbow.* Pen and ink with water colors, on paper, 12-13/16 x 11-3/4 inches. Executed ca.1780–1790.
Collection: Piancastelli, Rome, until 1901.
Literature: Richard P. Wunder, *Extravagant Drawings of the Eighteenth Century* (New York, 1962), no. 32.

The Cooper Union Museum, New York

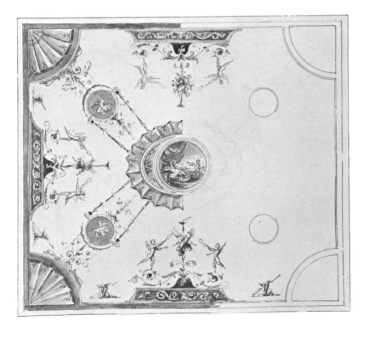

Giuseppe Bernardino Bison (Bisson)

Palmanova 1762—Milan 1844

Bison's artistic career was occupied chiefly with providing decorations for villas in North Italy—first near Venice, where he had been a student, and later in Lombardy. Although Neo-classic (sometimes even Neo-gothic) in style, his decorations reflect the spirit of Venetian art of the eighteenth century in their spritely elegance of line.

158 Design for a Ceiling

Pen, pencil, and water color, 8-1/8 x 9-1/4 inches. Executed ca.1790.

John Maxon, Chicago

159 Design
for a Painted Wall Decoration

Pencil, pen and ink, with water colors, on paper, 11-3/8 x
8-1/2 inches. Signed (lower right): Bison. Executed ca.
1805–1810.
Collections: Piancastelli, Rome, until 1904; Mrs. Edward
D. Brandegee, Brookline, Mass. (1904–1938).
Literature: Richard P. Wunder, *Extravagant Drawings of
the Eighteenth Century* (New York, 1962), no. 23.

The Cooper Union Museum, New York

Mauro Gandolfi

Bologna 1764—Bologna 1834

Mauro became a pupil of his father, the painter Gaetano Gandolfi, at the age of six. In his youth he traveled to France and the Netherlands, before returning to his native Bologna. In 1800 he, like Giani, went to Paris, where he was occupied chiefly with making reproductive engravings. In 1817 John Trumbull brought him from Bologna to Washington to make an engraving after Trumbull's *Signers of the Declaration of Independence*, but Congress would not meet his price, so Gandolfi returned to Italy.

160 Design
for a Painted Wall Decoration

Pencil, pen and ink, with water colors, on paper, 7-3/4 x
8-1/16 inches. Signed(?) (bottom center): Gandolfi. Executed ca.1800–1810.
Collections: Piancastelli, Rome, until 1904; Mrs. Edward
D. Brandegee, Brookline, Mass. (1904–1938).
Literature: Richard P. Wunder, *Extravagant Drawings of
the Eighteenth Century* (New York, 1962), no. 33.

The Cooper Union Museum, New York

Vincenzo Camuccini

Oil on canvas, 17-3/4 x 20 inches. Executed ca.1800.
A sketch for one of the decorations which Camuccini executed for Marc'Antonio Borghese.

Sir Anthony Blunt, Courtauld Institute of Art, London

Rome 1771—Rome 1844

Vincenzo's older brother, Pietro Camuccini, was an artist and art dealer. He, therefore, grew up as a part of the Roman artistic milieu. Vincenzo was the pupil of Domenico Corvi, under whom he made copies after Michelangelo and Raphael. By the end of the century he was producing original compositions. At about this time he decorated the ceilings of four rooms for Marc'Antonio Borghese with scenes from the youth of Paris. In 1806 he was made Princeps of the Accademia di San Luca and assumed a position in the forefront of the Roman school, which he held for the remainder of his life.

Giuseppe Bossi

Busto Arsizio 1777—Milan 1815

Bossi was a pupil of Appiani at the Academy in Milan. Among his most important works were decorations in the Brera Gallery and the Archaeological Museum in Milan. Bossi had an important collection of old master drawings as well as a rich library. He maintained a private school for painting. Among his numerous works was a copy of Leonardo's *Last Supper.*

162 *Adonis, Departing for the Hunt, Restrained by the Three Graces, with Venus*

Black chalk over grey wash heightened with white, 33 x 47 inches. Executed 1806–1807.
Literature: Hugh Honour has discovered a letter from Bossi to Canova, dated August 18, 1806, in which this drawing is described in detail. See D. Fortunato Federici, ed., *Lettere di Giuseppe Bossi ad Antonio Canova* (Padua, 1839), pp. 22, 28.

John Harris, London

Giovanni Battista (Titta) Lusieri

Active from 1781—died 1821

Titta Lusieri specialized in archaeologically exact water-color renderings of ancient monuments. He acted as traveling companion to Lords Hamilton and Elgin.

163 *The Baths of Caracalla from the Villa Mattei*

Water color, 18-1/8 x 25-1/8 inches. Signed and dated (lower left of original mount): Titta Lusier 1781. Inscribed (on back of mount by artist): Veduta delle Terme di Caracalla presa della Villa Mattei/Monte Celio.
Literature: Italian Drawings from the Museum's Collection, RISD (Providence, 1961), no. 95.

Museum of Art, Rhode Island School of Design

Livorno, 2nd half 18th century—active Rome ca.1800

Bargigli is a little-known architect. He held the title of Architetto del Consolato Romano; that is, he was one of the architects to the short-lived Roman Republic. In Napoleonic times he taught Bonaparte's talented sister, Elisa Baciochi, Grand Duchess of Tuscany, architectural and ornamental drawing.

164 *Allegory of the Poet Weaned from Envy or from Uncontrolled Passion to True Imagination*

Water color over ink, 17-15/16 x 22-3/4 inches. Signed and dated (lower left): Pietro Bargigli fecit 1791.
Collection: Robert Gilmor, purchased in Rome in 1843.
Literature: Anthony M. Clark, "Roman Eighteenth-Century Drawings in the Gilmor Collection," BMA *News,* XXIV (Spring 1961), 5-12, fig. 9.

The Baltimore Museum of Art, Robert Gilmor Collection On permanent loan from the Peabody Institute, Baltimore

Bartolomeo Pinelli

Rome 1781—Rome 1835

Bartolomeo was the son of the sculptor in wax, Giovanni Battista Pinelli. He began his training as an artist at a very early age, at the Accademia di San Luca and in Bologna. By about 1800 he was functioning as a professional artist. Pinelli performed as painter, draughtsman, engraver, lithographer, and sculptor. In 1807 Pinelli won a prize in life drawing at the Accademia di San Luca.

165 *Venus Watching Telemachus with Cupid on His Knee, while Mentor Observes in Disgust*

Pen and brown ink, brown and grey wash, over pencil, 18-9/16 x 23-1/4 inches. Signed and dated (lower right): Pinelli fecit Roma/1808.
One of a series of drawings by Pinelli in Chicago.

The Art Institute of Chicago, The Wirt Walker Fund

166 *Head of Silenus*

Anonymous, Italy(?)
Marble with inlaid eyes, 12-3/8 inches high.
The Metropolitan Museum of Art
Gift of J. Pierpont Morgan, 1917

167 *A Classical Hall*

Pen and wash, heightened with white, 11-3/16 x 15-3/16 inches.
Collections: Mayr-Fajt; Janos Scholz.
Donald Oenslager, New York

Lorenzo Sacchetti

Padua 1759–1829

Sacchetti began his career in Venice, where from 1781 to 1784 he was a pupil of Cerato and Fossati. He became a member of the Academy and a teacher there. He next went to Vienna in 1794 and in 1810 was put in charge of decorations for the court theatre. He was active as a designer of scenery in Prague and Brünn, as well as in Vienna. He also did fresco decorations in houses and churches in Venice and Padua, and in the North.

Gaspare Galliari

Treviglio 1761—Milan 1818

Gaspare Galliari was a member of a large family of Piedmontese artists, many of whom specialized in theatre designs. He was trained with his uncle, Fabrizio, who worked in Vienna. Gaspare was also active as a scenery designer in Milan, Genoa, and Venice. In 1810 he designed a monument for the battlefield where the battle of Arcole was fought.

168 *Aula Sepulcrale*

Water color, 18-1/4 x 25-1/2 inches.
Collection: Randolph Gunter.
One of a series of five designs by Gaspare Galliari in the same collection.

Donald Oenslager, New York

Antonio de Pian

Venice 1784—Vienna 1851

Antonio de Pian was a member of a family of theatre designers who were active chiefly in Vienna. He studied in Venice, where he was influenced by Canaletto, and in Vienna. In 1821 he was made Court Theatre Painter and in 1843 a member of the Vienna Academy.

169 *Entrance to a Classical Funeral Monument*

Water color on grey paper, 10-5/8 x 19-1/8 inches.
Collections: Mayr-Fajt; Janos Scholz.
Literature: George Freedley, (ed.), *Theatrical Designs from the Baroque through Neo-Classicism*, III (New York, 1940), pl. 8. Janos Scholz, ed., *Baroque and Romantic Stage Design* (New York, [1949]), pl. 105.

Donald Oenslager, New York

Mario Asprucci, the Younger

Rome 1764—Rome 1804

Mario Asprucci was the pupil of his father, the architect Antonio Asprucci. For Prince Borghese, Mario built two small temples, and a church outside Siena was constructed from his plans. Later in life, Asprucci was occupied with making copies after paintings.

Carlo Amati

Monza 1776—Milan 1852

Amati was a pupil first of Pollak. After his death in 1806, Amati worked with Zanoja on the facade of the Milan Cathedral. In 1817 he became a teacher of architecture at the Milan Academy. Amati's greatest work was the huge church of San Carlo Borromeo in Milan.

170 Design for a Sepulchral Monument

Pencil, pen and ink, with water colors, on paper, 10-9/16 x 18-1/4 inches. Executed ca.1800.
Collections: Piancastelli, Rome, until 1904; Mrs. Edward D. Brandegee, Brookline, Mass. (1904–1938).
Literature: Richard P. Wunder (ed.), *Summary Catalogue of Drawings by Identified Italian Architects in the Cooper Union Museum* (New York, 1964).

The Cooper Union Museum, New York

171 Design for a Sofa

Pen and ink with water colors, on paper, 9 x 15-1/8 inches. Signed and dated (lower right): Carolus Amati inv./1802.
Collection: Given by Miss Mildred Irby, New York, in 1959.

The Cooper Union Museum, New York

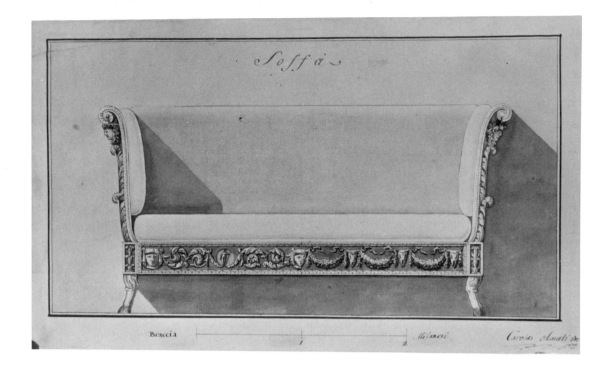

Soffà

Pietro Paolo Spagna

Rome 1793—Rome 1861

Pietro Paolo Spagna was a member of a family who had been silversmiths in Rome for several generations. He was made a master in 1817 and in that year became manager of his father's shop. In the same year, he and his father took over the shop of the famous silversmith, Giuseppe Valadier.

172 Pair of Tazzas

Silver gilt, 8 inches high. Marks: Rome marks and maker's marks mostly badly erased, but one is clearly that of Pietro Paolo Spagna. Engraved: Borghese arms. Executed ca.1820.

Collection: The style of these tazzas and the Borghese arms which they bear indicate that they were made to accompany the service of French silver which Napoleon is said to have given to his sister Pauline and her husband, Prince Camillo Borghese. According to the marks which they bear, these tazzas could have been made at any time between 1817 and 1861, but their style indicates that they were made toward the beginning of this period.

The Cleveland Museum of Art
Gift in Memory of Margaret Quayle Kerruish

Bertel Thorvaldsen

Copenhagen 1770—Copenhagen 1844

Thorvaldsen's father was a woodcarver by profession. At the age of twelve, he was already helping with his father's work, and in 1781 he entered the Academy. Abildgaard was the great man at the Academy, and he took the young Thorvaldsen under his wing. He won the highest gold medal in 1793. In 1796 Thorvaldsen left for Italy and arrived in Rome the next year. He remained in Rome until 1819, tied down by a long stream of commissions to be completed. His return to Denmark was a triumph but he stayed there only a short time. He was back in Rome again from 1820 to 1838, executing many commissions. His last years were passed in Denmark where great honors were given him. Thorvaldsen's style is based on that of Canova, but is more matter-of-factly realistic than that of the older master.

Marble, 21 x 35-1/2 inches.
Collection: Left by Thorvaldsen's will to the Museum, which opened in 1848.
Literature: F. M. Thiele, *Thorvaldsens Leben*, II (Leipzig, 1865), 101. Eugène Plon, *Thorvaldsen, Sa Vie et son Oeuvre* (Paris, 1874), pp. 319 ff., 422, fig. 321. *Catalogue of Thorvaldsens Museum* (Copenhagen, 1961), p. 46, no. 416.
A second version, done after the original of 1823. The subject is taken from *Anacreontea*, Song 3.

Thorvaldsens Museum, Copenhagen

Karl Friedrich von Schinkel

Neuruppin 1781—Berlin 1841

Schinkel was perhaps the greatest European architect of his time, yet the early part of his career was
devoted to the design of theatre sets. His serious
architectural career began only in 1816. Though his
theatre designs and some of his unexecuted architectural projects reflect a romantic interest in visual
drama, the great public buildings which Schinkel
designed for the Prussian capital of Berlin exhibited
a continuation of the rationalistic concept of architecture which had inspired Ledoux a generation
earlier.

174 *Sacrifice in a Temple*

Water color on paper, 15-1/2 x 20-5/8 inches. Executed
ca.1810–1820.

Nelson Gallery—Atkins Museum, Kansas City
Gift of Mr. Milton McGreevy

Franz Theobald Horny

Weimar 1798—Olevano 1824

Horny, whose father was a painter, studied first at the Weimar Art School. In 1816 he went to Rome with his friend Rumohr. Horny became associated with the idealistic young German artists, who called themselves the Nazarenes, in 1819. The ideas of this group were in many ways similar to the much later Pre-Raphaelite Brotherhood in England. Shortly thereafter he went to Olevano where he spent the last years of his short life.

175 *View of Olevano*

Pen and sepia wash, on pale green paper, 9-1/2 x 10-5/16 inches.
Collections· John Witt Randall; Belinda L. Randall.
Literature: Agnes Mongan and Paul J. Sachs, *Drawings in the Fogg Museum of Art* (Cambridge, 1940), p. 224, no. 433, fig. 212. Hans Tietze, *European Master Drawings in the United States* (New York, 1947), no. 123.

Fogg Art Museum, Harvard University
Bequest of Belinda L. Randall
from the John Witt Randall Collection

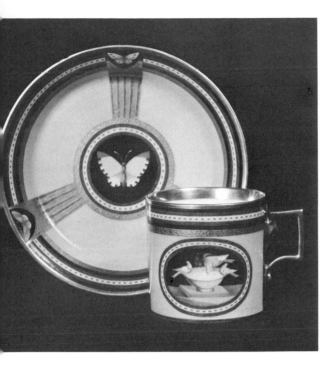

176 Cup and Saucer

Anonymous, Vienna, Austria

Porcelain: cup, 2-5/16 inches high; saucer, 5-5/8 inches in diameter. Marks: Vienna mark on both pieces. Executed ca.1800.

Literature: Helen S. Foote, "Important Additions to the Porcelain Collection," CMA *Bulletin*, XXXVIII (October 1951), 199-200, 203.

From about 1800 to 1810, the Vienna factory, directed by Konrad von Sorgenthal, led stylistically among European porcelain factories. The design of birds drinking from a basin which decorates the cup is derived from a Roman mosaic.

The Cleveland Museum of Art, Gift of R. Thornton Wilson in memory of his wife, Florence Ellsworth Wilson

Joseph Moreau

1772?–1830

Joseph Moreau (or "Moro" or "Morot") was a potter or painter active at the St. Petersburg porcelain factory in the early nineteenth century. He is probably identical with Denis-Joseph Moreau who was a painter at the Sèvres factory from 1807 to 1815.

177 Vase

Porcelain decorated with gilding, 22 inches high. Inscribed (inside rim): Moreau. Executed ca.1820.
Made at the Russian Imperial Porcelain Factory, St. Petersburg.

The Cleveland Museum of Art
In memory of Arthur G. McKee

Joseph Michael Gandy

London 1771—London 1843

Gandy was first the pupil of Wyatt and later studied at the Royal Academy School. He went to Italy in 1794 and returned to England in 1798. He was then employed by Sir John Soane, who became his chief patron and for whom he worked irregularly for the rest of his life. Although Gandy was trained as an architect, few buildings were constructed from his designs. He is better known today for the architectural fantasies which he painted and exhibited regularly at the Royal Academy.

178 *An Imperial Palace for Sovereigns of the British Empire, Project No. 2*

Water color, 30 x 53 inches. Executed ca.1824.
Exhibited: London, Royal Academy, 1824.
Literature: John Summerson, *Heavenly Mansions: the Vision of J. M. Gandy* (London, 1949), p. 131.
Royal Institute of British Architects, London

179 *Fantastic Classical Ruins*

Water color on paper, 12-3/16 x 17-15/16 inches.
Nelson Gallery—Atkins Museum, Kansas City
Gift of Mr. Milton McGreevy

Sir Charles Eastlake

Plymouth 1793—Pisa 1865

Eastlake was a pupil at the school of the Royal
Academy in 1809, and made his debut at the exhibitions of the British Institution in 1813. After working for a time in Paris, Eastlake went on to Italy in
1816. He did not return to London until 1830, but
had nevertheless exhibited his pictures there regularly while living in Italy. He enjoyed a career of
official success in England. He was made president
of the Royal Academy in 1850 and the first director
of the National Gallery in 1855.

180 *The Celian Hill from the Palatine*

Oil on canvas, 12-3/4 x 17-1/8 inches. Signed (lower edge,
left center): C. L. Eastlake 1823.
Exhibited: Museum of Art, Rhode Island School of Design, The Age of Canova, 1957, p. 12, no. 54.

    Museum of Art, Rhode Island School of Design

Thomas Morgan and John Sanders

London

The firm of furniture dealers, Morgan and Sanders, was one of the most important in London in the early nineteenth century. Their wares were often featured in Ackermann's *Repository*. . . . One of the specialties of Morgan and Sanders seems to have been multi-purpose furniture.

181 Globe-shaped Sewing and Writing Table

Probably made by Morgan and Sanders

Wood with painted and marquetry decorations, 38-1/2 inches high. Executed ca.1810–1815.
Collection: Mrs. J. Pierpont Morgan.
Literature: James Parker, "A Regency Sewing and Writing Table by Morgan and Sanders," MMA *Bulletin*, XXII (November 1963), 124-132.
In 1808 Morgan and Sanders acquired from George Remington rights to manufacture globe-shaped tables. Remington's patent ran until 1828.

The Metropolitan Museum of Art
Gift of Mrs. Paul G. Pennoyer, 1962

Paul Storr

London 1771—London 1844

Storr was apprenticed to a plate-worker, Andrew Fogelberg, from 1785 to 1792. After working with William Frisbee for a few years, he set up on his own in 1796. In 1802 he became the partner of Digby Scott. By 1811 he was a partner in the firm of Rundell, Bridge and Rundell. In 1819 he set up an independent shop, and in 1822 became a partner of John Mortimer. Their partnership continued until 1839, when Storr retired. Storr is considered the most important English silversmith of his time.

182 Pair of Wine Coolers

Silver gilt, 11 inches high. Marks: Usual London marks, maker's mark, date letter "N." Inscribed: RUNDELL BRIDGE ET RUNDELL AURIFICES REGIS ET PRINCIPIS WALLIAE LONDINI FECERUNT.
One of an identical pair of wine coolers, but with additional stands, is illustrated in N. M. Penzer, *Paul Storr* (London, 1954), pp. 136-137, pl. XXIX.

The Museum of Fine Arts, Boston, Theodora Wilbour Fund
in memory of Charlotte Beebe Wilbour

183 Covered Ewer

Silver, 9-1/8 inches high. Marks on cover: Maker's mark, lion passant, date letter "R." Marks on ewer: Maker's mark, lion passant, date letter "R," leopard's head, king's head. Dated: 1812–1813.
Collection: Viscount Ossory, Dublin.

City Art Museum of St. Louis

William Rush

Philadelphia 1756—Philadelphia 1833

As a youth Rush learned the art of ship carving in the shop of Edward Cutbush in Philadelphia. After the Revolution he set up shop on his own there. Rush worked chiefly as a carver of decorations for ships, but he also executed wood sculpture for other purposes. He was a promoter of the Columbianum and the Pennsylvania Academy.

184 Mercury

Painted walnut, 44-1/2 inches high. Executed ca.1828.
Literature: Henri Marceau, *William Rush, The First Native American Sculptor* (Philadelphia, 1937), p. 57, no. 47.
Originally stood atop a small circular temple on Fairmount near the present Philadelphia Museum of Art.

The Commissioners of Fairmount Park
Courtesy of the Philadelphia Museum of Art

John Vanderlyn

Kingston, New York 1775—Kingston 1852

Vanderlyn studied first under Archibald Robertson
and then for a few months under Gilbert Stuart, before being sent to Paris by his patron, Aaron Burr,
in 1796. He was there for five years, returned to New
York briefly in 1801, and then was again in Europe
for twelve years, two of them in Rome. He returned
to America in 1815. In 1837 he was commissioned to
paint *Landing of Columbus* for the Capitol in Washington, and returned to Europe to execute it. Embit-
tered by public indifference and artistic rivalries,
Vanderlyn retired to a life of poverty in his native
town.

185 *Ariadne Asleep on the Island of Naxos*

Oil on canvas, 68 x 87 inches. Signed and dated (lower
left): J. Vanderlyn fect Parisiis 1814.
Collections: Purchased from the artist by Asher B. Durand
in 1831; purchased from the Durand Estate by Joseph
Harrison, Jr.; presented to the Pennsylvania Academy by
Mrs. Joseph Harrison, Jr., in 1878.
Exhibited: Philadelphia, Special Exhibition, Great Cen-
tral Fair, Logan Square, Benefit U. S. Sanitary Commis-
sion, 1864.
Literature: Oliver Larkin, *Art and Life in America* (New
York, 1949), pp. 131, 134-135, 143, 242.

The Pennsylvania Academy of the Fine Arts

John Frankenstein

Germany ca.1816—East New York, New York 1881

John Frankenstein came with his family, most of whom were artists, to Cincinnati in 1831. He began painting portraits at the age of fifteen. By 1839 he had moved to Philadelphia, where he worked for several years. He was back in Cincinnati by 1847 and two years later moved to Springfield, Ohio. He returned to Cincinnati in 1856, at which time he turned from portrait painting to portrait sculpture. He went to New York in 1875. He spent the last years of his life as an apparently poverty-stricken recluse, but after his death a considerable amount of money was found in his possession.

186 *Self-Portrait*

Oil on canvas, 24 x 20 inches. Executed ca.1835–1840.
Victor D. Spark, New York

Horatio Greenough

Boston 1805—Somerville, Massachusetts 1852

As a young man, Greenough was encouraged by Washington Allston to study sculpture. After graduating from Harvard in 1824, he set out for Italy, where he was destined to spend most of his life. He was back in America in 1826, and left again in 1829, when he went to study marble carving in Carrara, and later settled in Florence. He received several government commissions, notably for his large seated figure of Washington, and he became the first American sculptor to achieve more than local fame. He decided to return to America to settle permanently in Newport, Rhode Island, in 1851, but he died the next year.

187 *Castor and Pollux*

Marble, 34-1/2 x 45 inches.
The Museum of Fine Arts, Boston
Gift of Mrs. Horatio Greenough, 1892

Hiram Powers

Woodstock, Vermont 1805—Florence 1873

Powers moved as a child to New York State and later lived near Cincinnati. From 1829 to 1834 he worked in Dorfeuille's Western Museum in Cincinnati. In the latter year he moved to Washington, where he did several portrait busts. In 1837 he sailed for Europe with his family. After passing a few months in Paris, he settled permanently in Florence. Powers was a successful and widely acclaimed sculptor in his day.

188 *Proserpine*

Marble, 25 inches high. Signed (on back): H. Powers, Sculp.
Literature: Catalogues of the Layton Collection (Milwaukee, 1907 and 1921). Albert Ten Eyck Gardner, *Yankee Stonecutters* (New York, 1945), p. 15.
Powers is said to have made fifty copies of *Proserpine* for which he charged $400 each. The design is based upon a Roman portrait bust which was formerly in the Towneley Collection and is now in the British Museum.

Milwaukee Art Center, Layton Collection

Samuel McIntire

Salem, Massachusetts 1757—Salem 1811

Samuel McIntire was famous as an architect, sculptor, and designer and carver of furniture. His native city of Salem remained the center of his activity throughout his life. His father, from whom he received his earliest training, was a housewright. Before 1780 he had established a reputation of his own as a designer and builder of houses. In 1793 McIntire came under the influence of the Boston architect, Charles Bulfinch, who had traveled in England and had brought to America the early Neo-classic architectural style of the brothers Adam. McIntire was perhaps the best practitioner of all of his occupations in the Salem of his day.

189 Chair

Mahogany and ebony, 38 inches high.
Collection: Derby family, Salem.
Literature: Henry H. Hawley, "A McIntire Chair," CMA *Bulletin,* L (November 1963), 249-251.

The Cleveland Museum of Art
Purchase from the J. H. Wade Fund

Charles-Honoré Lannuier

Chantilly 1779—New York 1819

The son of a Parisian *ébéniste*, Lannuier came to
New York about 1803. He brought with him the
necessary skill for making furniture in the French
Louis XVI style, and he was among the first cabinetmakers in America to introduce the newly fasnion-
able Empire style. He worked in New York, and
most of his furniture was made for persons in that
city and in the Hudson Valley, but his reputation
spread, and he also worked for other patrons along
the Atlantic coast.

190 Armchair

Mahogany with black, gilt, and gilt bronze decorations, 36
inches high. Executed ca.1815.
Collection: James Bosley, Baltimore.
Literature: Lorraine Waxman Pearce, "Lannuier in the
President's House," *Antiques*, LXXXI (January 1962),
94-95.
Part of a suite of furniture once owned by James Bosley.

The Maryland Historical Society, Baltimore

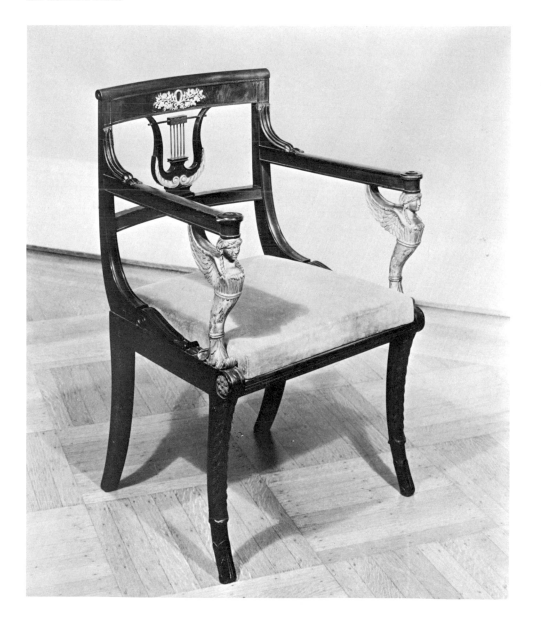

191 Covered Bowl

Fletcher and Gardiner (active Philadelphia 1814–1838)
Silver, 6 inches high. Marks: Maker's mark and date. Engraved (on bottom): Presented by the Citizens of Baltimore to/com. John Rogers/in testimony of their sense of the important aid/offered by him in defense of Baltimore/ on the 12th & 13th of Sept. 1814. Executed 1831.
Exhibited: The Newark Museum, Classical America, 1815–1845, pp. 97, 104, no. 112.
The Maryland Historical Society, Baltimore

192 Couch

Anonymous, New York
Pine, painted black, with gilt stenciled decorations, upholstered in gold morine with red and black tapes, 33-1/8 inches high, 78 inches wide. Executed ca.1825–1835.
Literature: Robert C. Smith, "Late Classical furniture in the United States, 1820–1850," *Antiques*, LXXIV (December 1958), 520-521. Helen Comstock, *American Furniture* (New York, 1962), no. 538.
Yale University Art Gallery
Mabel Brady Garvan Collection

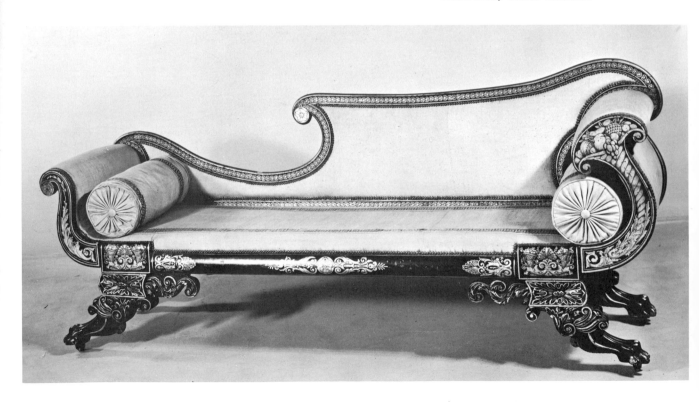

Eugène Delacroix

Chareton Saint-Maurice 1798—Paris 1863

Delacroix was one of the great innovators in the history of Western painting. He was a pupil of Guérin, and his earliest works—for example, the *Dante and Virgil Crossing the Styx*, which was exhibited at the Salon of 1822—reveal traces of Neo-classicism. Soon after that date, Delacroix's work changed, and the full Romantic style in painting was realized.

193 *Page of Seven Antique Medals*

Lithograph, 10 9/16 x 9 inches. Signed and dated (lower left): E. Delacroix/1825.
Collection: Alfred Lebrun, Paris (Lugt 140).
Literature: Loys Delteil, *Le Peintre-Graveur Illustré,* XIII (Paris, 1908), 13, no. 45, state IV/V.
One of seven lithographs made by Delacroix which reproduce ancient coins and medals. He made these specifically to demonstrate that it was possible, even when reproducing ancient works of art, to abandon the linear convention of Neo-classicism.

The Cleveland Museum of Art
Mr. and Mrs. Charles G. Prasse Collection
Gift of Leona E. Prasse

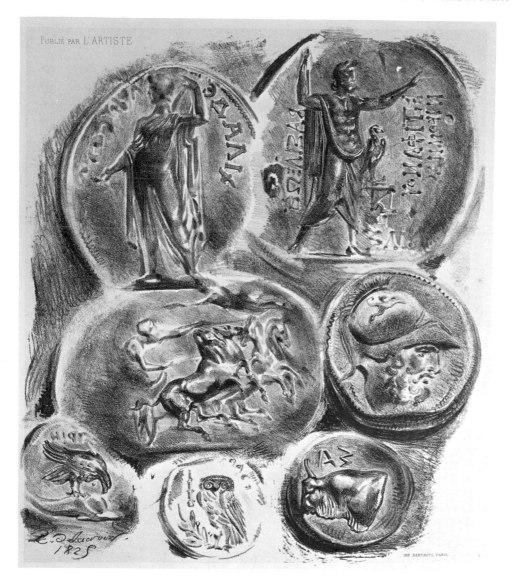

List of Lenders

Index of Artists

COLOPHON

Printed by lithography on Mohawk Superfine Text
by Great Lakes Lithograph Company, Cleveland.
Composed in Bodoni types by Davis & Warde, Inc., Pittsburgh.
Bound in Holliston Zeppelin by Russell-Rutter Company, Inc., New York.
Design and typography by Merald E. Wrolstad.

Riverside City College Library,
Riverside, California